GW00535799

THE
GRINTON MINES

(Including Fremington and Ellerton)

by

L.O. Tyson and I.M. Spensley
with R.F. White

The Society gratefully acknowledges the receipt of a grant from the Yorkshire Dales National Park towards the cost of this publication.

A
MONOGRAPH
OF THE
NORTHERN MINE RESEARCH SOCIETY
MAY 1995

ISSN 0308 2199

ISBN 0 901450 42 1

© L.O. TYSON, I.M. SPENSLEY & R.F. White 1995

Typeset in 10 point Times New Roman.

PRINTED

by

RYTON TYPING SERVICE

29 Ryton Street, Worksop,

Notts.

for the publishers

THE NORTHERN MINE RESEARCH SOCIETY
KEIGHLEY U.K.

Cover Illustration:
The How Smelt Mill at Grinton. Barker collection.

THE GRINTON MINES
(including Fremington and Ellerton)

CONTENTS

INTRODUCTION   8

EARLY HISTORY   8
James Phillips (1583-1597)   12

THE MARRIOTT FAMILY (1660-1736)   15
The First Crown Mineral Rights Dispute   16
The Dispute between Sir Solomon Swale & Roger Hillary   16
Reginald Marriott's dispute with Sir Solomon Swale   17
Lord Wharton's Trespass   18
Marriott's peaceful tenure   20

THE MOORE FAMILY (1736-1765)   24
Edmund Moore   24
Mrs Frances Moore   24
Expansion of the Mines   26
The Harker Dispute   27

WILLIAM KNIGHTON (1765-1771)   30
The Chauncy Townsend Dispute   30
George Jackson's Survey   31
Trouble at T'Mill   32

THE KNIGHTON, READSHAW PARTNERSHIP (1771-1817)   33
Summer Lodge. A new mine and a new dispute   35
The New Adventurers   37
The New Inheritors   38
The Second Summer Lodge Dispute   39

THE MORLEY FAMILY (1817-1854)   43
Josias Readshaw Morley   43
Francis Morley   44
Stephen Eddy's report   46
The Consortium   47
The Harland-Morley Affair   48
The Declining Years   48
The Kinnaird Commission   51
The Final Push   51

THE CHARLESWORTH FAMILY (1855-1946)   53
Sale of the Mines   54
The Swaledale Mining Association   55
The Grinton Mining & Smelting Company Ltd   55

THE GRINTON MINES   58
    Devis Hole   58
    Grinton How   59
    Grovebeck   66
    Harkerside   70
    Brownagill and Guy   71
    Whitaside   72
    Summer Lodge   80

THE ELLERTON MINES   84

THE FREMINGTON MINES   91
    Background   91
    The Whartons of Gillingwood   91
    The Whartons of Skelton Castle   95
    The Swann Bank   96

OTHER MINERALS   99
    Coal   99
    Stone   99

THE SMELT MILLS   100
    How or Low mill   100
    Grovebeck mill   104
    New mill   104
    Scott's mill   104
    Summer Lodge mill   105
    Ellerton mill   105

THE GRINTON LOW OR HOW MILL COMPLEX   107
    The map evidence   107
    Previous studies   107
    The buildings   109
    Peat house   119
    The flue   121
    The water supply   122
    Other earthworks   122
    The lime kilns   123
    Logistical problems   123

THE CONSOLIDATION PROGRAMME   124
    Emergency works   124
    The mill   124
    The beck   126
    The peat house   126

PRODUCTION FIGURES   128

PLATES

1	Cogden Gill Deep Level, begun 1861	50
2	Grinton Lodge	53
3	Building at the portal of Smithy Level at Whitaside Mine	71
4	Waterwheel pit for the crusher at Whitaside Mine	73
5	Bouse teams at Summer Lodge Mine	82
6	Grinton How smelt mill, looking north-east	101
7	How smelt mill and peat house, looking west down line of flue	102
8	How smelt mill, east side, showing egress of flue	103
9	The now demolished building near the How smelt mill	108
10	The now demolished building near the How smelt mill	108
11	How smelt mill: masonry arches for the ore-hearths	110
12	How smelt mill: timber frame for the blowing system	112
13	How smelt mill: launder and bearings for the blowing system	114
14	How smelt mill during re-roofing	117
15	How smelt mill and peat house, looking south-west	119
16	How smelt mill: access hole in the flue	121
17	How smelt mill: emergency consolidation work, 1977	125

FIGURES

1	Grinton and Fremington Mines	10
2	Plan of Mr Marriott's lead mines at Grinton How, October 1717	21
3	Plan of the area around Bloody Vale in dispute with Lord Pomfret	36
4	Devis Mine	60
5	Grinton How Mines	64
6	Grovebeck Mine	67
7	Grovebeck Mine	69
8	Whitaside Mines	74
9	Whitaside Mine	77
10	Summer Lodge Mine	81
11	Ellerton Moor and Devis Mines	86
12	Grinton How smelt mill (OS 1/2500 sheet 52.8 Yorks NR 1893)	111
13	Grinton How smelt mill (OS 1/2500 sheet 52.8 Yorks NR 1913)	113
14	Floor level plan of Grinton How smelt mill	115
15	Principal roof truss at Grinton How smelt mill	116

MANUSCRIPT SOURCES

Barker MSS, Healaugh.
Clarkson MSS.
Holliday of Mount St John MSS.
Skelton MSS, Skelton Castle, Cleveland.

ABBREVIATIONS

DRO D/HH	Durham County Records Office. Hanby Holmes Mss.
MPPBL	Marrick Priory MSS, Brotherton Library, Leeds University.
NCMRS	Northern Cavern & Mine Research Society – Records.
NMRS	Northern Mine Research Society – Records.
NYCRO	North Yorkshire County Records Office.
NRO	Northumberland Record Office.
PRO	Public Records Office, Chancery Lane - Crown Estates Papers.
PRO	Public Records Office, Kew - Board of Trade Papers.
YML	York Minster Library, Hailstone MSS.

ACKNOWLEDGEMENTS
The authors would like to thank the following people for their assistance and for access to private records: J.L. & S. Barker of Healaugh; L.B. Holliday of Mount St John; Anthony Wharton of Skelton Castle; the late Elsie Pedley; John Goodchild; Clifford Clarkson; Mike Gill, and Edward Pedley.

We are also grateful to those who have placed their records in the North Yorkshire County Record Office at Northallerton, and the County Archivist for permission to quote from these papers.

Excerpts from the Hanby Holmes MSS at Durham Record Office are reproduced by the permission of Mr R.J. Hanby Holmes and the County Archivist of Durham.

Material from the Hailstone MSS at York Minster Library is used with the kind permission of the Dean and Chapter of York Minster and the Archivist.

EDITOR'S NOTE
The first section of this monograph takes us step by step through the history of the Grinton mining field, while the section to page 105 describes the mines themselves and the smelt mills. The third section deals with the consolidation and archaeological work at the How smelt mill carried out by the Yorkshire Dales National Park. Inevitably this approach has led to some repetition, but this has been kept to a minimum.

Please note that many of the sites mentioned in this monograph are on private land and visitors are asked to respect this.

INTRODUCTION

The Grinton Mines are situated on the south side of the valley of the River Swale in North Yorkshire. The mining field has six distinct sets which come together under the group title of the Grinton Mines. The most easterly set is Cogden/Grinton Moor, followed in turn westward by Grinton How, Grovebeck, Harkerside, Whitaside and finally Summer Lodge. After 1571 a lease of the Grinton mines also included those in the manor of Fremington on the north side of the dale.

The minerals at Grinton belonged to the Crown, but, owing to an error in 1599, the surface rights were lost, causing problems for lessees. The Crown's possession of the Grinton mines was not a peaceful one and two lengthy disputes were fought in the Court of Chancery to establish the Crown title. The western boundary at Summer Lodge was the subject of disputes lasting well into the late 19th century.

The nature of the mineral deposits at Grinton is entirely different from those of North Swaledale which consist of regular vein deposits. In Grinton the ore was found in flots which were highly remunerative to the first discoverers, but left those who followed chasing a dream of hidden wealth in the many expensive trials which sought to emulate the first finds.

EARLY HISTORY

As in most of the Yorkshire Dales, the earliest evidence for human activity in the Grinton area are scatters of worked flint tools used by Mesolithic hunters some 10,000 years ago. The oldest monuments so far discovered in the Grinton area are Bronze Age burial mounds. Extensive remains of field systems and settlement platforms point to a sizeable community in late-prehistoric – Romano-British times, while at least one coin hoard, dating from the second century AD, has been found in Grinton. No contemporary lead working sites have been identified, but early settlers were probably aware of the mineral resources of the area and exploited them either through shallow surface workings or stream deposits.[1] The large hillside enclosure known as Maiden Castle may be late-prehistoric in date, but may instead be contemporary with the massive cross-valley dyke system known as the Grinton-Fremington dykes. These are now believed to have been built in the fifth to seventh centuries AD to mark the boundary between British and Anglian peoples. Andrew Fleming has suggested that the economic *raison d'être* of the British kingdom, or polity, in Upper Swaledale was the lead industry.[2]

After the Norman Conquest, Swaledale became part of the Honour of Richmond. Early in the 12th century, it was under the Lordship of Count Stephen of Brittany and upon the marriage of his daughter Maude to Walter de Gant it was given as part of her dowry in return for military service at Richmond Castle. In 1125 Maude gave the Church of St Andrew in Grinton with some land for its upkeep to Bridlington Priory, which her husband had founded in about 1113. Subsequent grants of land by the Gants increased the holdings of the Priory as far west as Haverdale Beck by the beginning of the 14th century thus establishing a Manor of Grinton in a parochial form. The mineral rights were excepted in the original grant and retained as part of the Honour of Richmond, eventually passing to the Crown.[3]

The first documentary evidence for lead being mined in Swaledale occurs in the Pipe Roll for 1181 when Walter de Gant sent lead to be used in the building of Waltham Abbey.[4] It is highly likely that he also sent lead to Bridlington Priory. Further evidence of the importance of the Swaledale mines, which included Grinton, was the issue in 1219 by Henry III of a Mandate confirming a previous one which guaranteed the miners of Swaledale the right to work unmolested in return for a Royalty to the Crown.[5] This gave them privileges similar to those enjoyed by the free mining districts of Derbyshire and Alston Moor.

Evidence of who was working the Grinton mines does not occur until 1504 when the Whitaside mines are mentioned in the will of Christopher Conyers of Marske. He was related by marriage to the powerful Metcalfes of Nappa in Wensleydale, the main Crown lessees of all the lead mines in the Honours of Richmond and Middleham. In his will Conyers bequeathed to his wife Elizabeth "*halfe a more mere at Whitnowsyke* (an early spelling of Whitaside) *in the workyng of James Atkinson and halfe another more mere in the workyng of Edmund Tod*".[6]

These and earlier miners smelted their ore at bales, which were wood-burning wind-blown hearths built on hillsides so as to catch the prevailing wind. Manually operated bellows were sometimes used to blow the fire, especially where slag was being resmelted. The activities of smelters (also called brenners or ore burners) denuded the dale of its wood. This was such a problem by the 1530s, that Leland observed that "*the woode that they brenne theire lead is brought owte of the parts of the shire, and owt of Dirhamshire*". Bales have been found on Harkerside and near Grinton How.[7]

In July 1531 Sir James Metcalfe took a new lease of the lead and coal mines for 21 years, paying the Crown 1/9th duty.[8] The income generated from this lease was used to pay the wages of the garrison at Berwick Castle. The mines in Arkengarth-dale were excepted as they had been granted to William Conyers of Marske. Conyers, as the main sublessee from Metcalfe, let the Harkerside and Whitaside mines to his nephew, Sir Francis Bigod of Settrington. After Bigod was executed in 1537 for his part in the Pilgrimage of Grace, the Crown reclaimed them.[9]

When Bridlington Priory was dissolved in 1537 and William Wood the Prior executed for his part in the Pilgrimage of Grace, the priory lands at Grinton became Crown property. The church of St Andrew was appropriated by the Crown, which then farmed out the rectory and tithes for an annual rent of £41. The enclosed lands were held in Customary Tenure by leases which had been granted by the Priory as early as 1483 to encourage their tenants.[10]

James Phillips, Collector of Crown Rents, ordered a survey of the Lordship of Grinton in 1538 to determine the value of the recently acquired lands and mines. Richard Pollard, one of the Surveyors General, reported: "*No profit growing from the farm of the lead mines on Grenton Moor because it lays unoccupied by reason of the poverty of the tenants of the Lordship of Grenton*".[11]

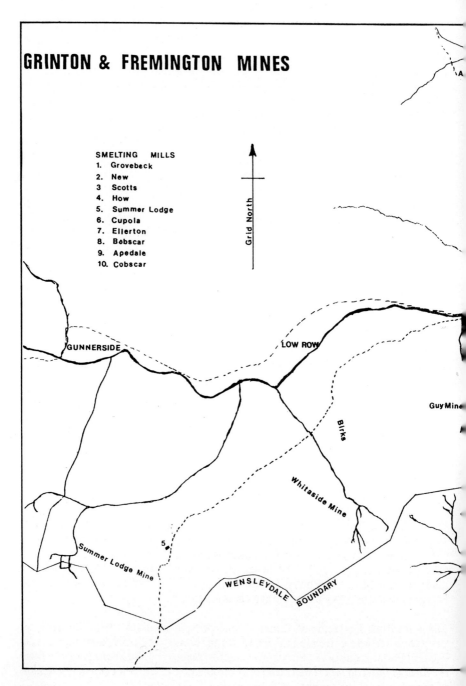

GRINTON & FREMINGTON MINES

SMELTING MILLS
1. Grovebeck
2. New
3 Scotts
4. How
5. Summer Lodge
6. Cupola
7. Ellerton
8. Bobscar
9. Apedale
10. Cobscar

Grid North

Fig.1

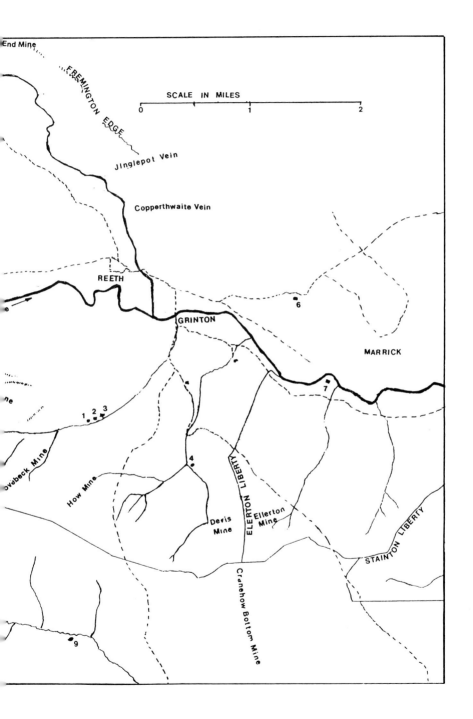

End Mine

FREMINGTON EDGE

SCALE IN MILES

0   1   2

Jinglepot Vein

Copperthwaite Vein

REETH

GRINTON

MARRICK

6

7

1 2 3

ovebeck Mine

How Mine

4

Devis Mine

ELLERTON LIBERTY

Ellerton Mine

STAINTON LIBERTY

Cranehow Bottom Mine

9

Grinton Moor probably included Harkerside and Whitaside, but this lack of precision in defining the extent of the wastes led to confusion in the next century when the value of the mines was realised and Crown ownership challenged. More confusion arises as St Andrew's was then the only church in Upper Swaledale, which was described as the Parish of Grinton for administrative purposes.

After the death of Sir James Metcalfe, the lease of 1531 was surrendered and a new one for a further term of 21 years was granted to his son, Christopher Metcalfe, in 1544, at a payment of 1/9th duty to the Crown.[12] In 1550 a 21 year lease of a portion of the ore raised at Grinton, which had formerly belonged to Sir Francis Bigod, was granted to Humphrey Cholwick at an annual rent of 50 shillings.[13]

In 1574/5 the Court of Exchequer ordered Lawrence Meries, one of its officers, to survey the Grinton and Fremington mines and report on any yearly rents due to the Crown. Two local miners, John Blades and John Douglas, were called to give evidence for the survey. Douglas stated that lead had been got in Grinton over the past 14 years but *"those that have made search for mines in the Manor of Grinton and was at great charges and got nothing to my knowledge but lost by their own labour and charges such notwithstanding I could be contented to give five shillings or 6s 8d by the year for it so that no other person deal with it save me"*. One of the prospectors was John Uvedale who was Lord of the Manor of Marrick and owner of mines there. It also appears from the evidence that the custom of the manor permitted trials for ore to be made in the wastes with the object of obtaining a lease from the Crown if successful. Some doubt as to the truthfulness of the evidence given by Douglas was expressed by the Commission who believed he was playing down the value of the mines and making a veiled offer for a lease.[14]

JAMES PHILLIPS 1583-1597

The first specific lease of the Grinton Mines was granted to Henry, Lord Scrope, and Arthur Phillips. It was to start on the 17th of February 1583 for a term of 21 years at an annual rent of 20 shillings and a fine of £40.[15] This lease names the mines at Harkerside and Whitaside, the oversight in the earlier Survey now being rectified. Also included in this lease were the Fremington mines at the same rent of 20 shillings a year. These rents were to remain unchanged for 300 years.

An interesting series of coincidences then occurred with this lease. The father of Arthur Phillips, one of the lessees, was James Phillips of Brignall, an officer for the Royal Woods, Mines and Lands. He was responsible for collecting taxes for the area and also acted as bailiff for the Queen's Woods at Grinton and was agent for Lord Scrope's estates in Wensleydale.[16]

James Phillips was described as a dominating and thoroughly unscrupulous man in the many lawsuits in which he became involved. He was accused of stripping and plundering the estates where he was steward. Tenants were thrown out and people were forced into expensive law suits which usually bankrupted them. This enabled him to get the property involved cheaply, and he also forced loans with no intention of repaying. He is even reputed to have been a practitioner of the Black

Arts. During the reign of Henry VIII, he and his brother were accused of sorcery and forced to flee from Court after a dead cat was discovered in their apartments.

Undeterred, Phillips soon regained considerable influence at Court when Queen Elizabeth succeeded her sister. This was demonstrated when Joan, the only daughter and heiress of William Conyers of Marske, became a ward of the Queen. Using his influence, Phillips persuaded the Queen to allow his second son, Arthur, to marry the Conyers' heiress, despite the wishes of her family. By this marriage Arthur gained possession of the Manor of Marske, the lead mines, and considerable lands and property in the Richmond and Cleveland areas.

In one of Phillips' many legal disputes, Avery Uvedale, holder of the impropriate Rectory of East Grinton from the Crown, accused him of using his position as bailiff for the woods in Grinton to plunder the timber and sell it off for his own gain. Given Phillips' nature, it is most likely he did the same with the mines once his son gained the lease, using his position as Collector of Taxes to conceal their true value. It is possible that Phillips smelted ore from other mines in the area, using the large supplies of timber at his disposal. It is also possible that much of the timber was sent to his smelt mill at Marske.

Letters Patent were issued on November 10th 1599 granting the Manor of Grinton, which included land at Grinton, Harkerside, Haverdale and Summer Lodge, to Richard Wiseman and Francis Fitch, citizens of London, for the sum of £1463 9s 2d. The Crown reserved the church, vicarage and *"uno mineri plumbi being within the Manors of Fremington and Grinton of the annual rent of 40 shillings"*.[17] In 1605 Wiseman sold almost all the manor to the tenants at 120 years' purchase, thereby making them freeholders. What remained of his title, plus three cottages, were sold in 1610 for £60 to Rev. Henry Simpson, the vicar of Grinton, who in turn sold them in 1622 to Robert Hillary of Grays Inn. It should be pointed out that the title *"Manor"* was an administrative term only. As the land was held under customary tenancy (a form of copyhold) and later freehold, no Court Baron could be held by the owner of the lands, making it merely a *"Reputed"* manor rather than an actual manor with the rights attendant to such.[18]

A curious oversight which was to have dire consequences for later Crown lessees occurred in the sale to Wiseman and Fitch. The Letters Patent included a grant of the wastes and moors where the mines were situated and it is difficult to comprehend this gross error by the Crown solicitor. An even more glaring oversight was made by these two land speculators for they made no provision for the surface rights for the unenclosed lands after the sales of 1605 and title to them disappeared until 1678.

After the death of Arthur Phillips in 1597, the mines reverted to the Crown. A survey of the Honours of Richmond and Middleham made in 1605 shows that all the mines in both Honours, apart from Arkengarthdale, were leased by Humphrey Wharton.[19] He was an important Crown official in the North, holding the position of Receiver General of Land Revenues for the Archdeaconry of Richmond and the counties of Durham and Northumberland.[20] This lease was renewed on May 1st 1628 to Wharton and Henry Lord Scrope for a further term of 21 years.[21]

Humphrey Wharton belonged to a younger branch of the Lords Wharton who owned the neighbouring manor of Healaugh. He had purchased the Gillingwood Estate near Richmond in 1609 and built the Gilling Smelt Mill.[22] Ore from his Grinton and Fremington mines was sent there for smelting, prior to being shipped out via Boroughbridge.[23] Major Norton of Richmond, Collector of the King's Taxes in the North, accounted for 18 shillings' rent for the Grinton mines paid by Humphrey Wharton in 1641.[24]

REFERENCES

1   King. A.   *Early Pennine Settlement* (Clapham: Dalesman, 1975) p.46.

2   Fleming, A. "Swadal, Swar (and Erechwydd?): early medieval polities in Upper Swaledale" *Landscape History* (forthcoming 1995).

3   VCH Grinton, p.236. Clay, C.T. *Early Yorkshire Charters* (Yorkshire Record Society, Vol.5, 1936) p.340.

4   Raistrick, A. & Jennings, B.   *A History of Lead Mining in the Pennines* (London: Longmans, 1965) p.25.

5   VCH Grinton. p.237. Raistrick & Jennings, p.55.

6   Tyson, L.O. "Mining and Smelting in the Marske Area" *British Mining*, No.50 (1994), pp.24-40. Raine, J.Marske (Yorkshire Archaeological & Topographical Journal, Vol.6, 1881) p.228. Raistrick & Jennings p.56.

7   Smith, L.T. (Ed)   *Itinerary of John Leland, Vol.4* (London: 1908). Barker, J.L. ' ' B a l e Hills in Swaledale & Arkengarthdale" *British Mining*, No.8 (1978), pp.49-54. Barker, J.L. & White, R.   "Early Smelting in Swaledale: A Further Look" in Willies, L. & Cranstone, D. (Eds) *Boles and Smeltmills* (Historical Metallurgy Society, 1992), pp.15-19.

8   Metcalfe, W.C. & G.   *Records of the family of Metcalfe* (1891) p.59. PRO. Patent Roll SC6/Henry VIII/4166. 35 Henry VIII. Raistrick & Jennings p.56.

9   DRO. D/HH/6/4/2.

10   Barker MSS. Charlesworth v Broderick.

11   PRO. CRES 34/211, File 1441.

12   PRO. Letters & Papers Henry VIII. Metcalfe Family Records p.59.

13   YML. Hailstone MSS, Box 5, Bundle 41.

14   PRO. CRES 34/211, File 1441.

15   PRO. CRES 34/211, File 1441, LRRO 3/85.

16   Raine, *Marske*, p.233. Tyson, *Marske*.

17   DRO. D/HH/6/4/1. Patent Roll. 41 Elizabeth part 18. M 18.

18   Barker MSS. Charlesworth v Broderick.

19   Willan & Crossley (Eds).   *Three 17th Century Yorkshire Surveys* (YAS Record Series, 1941), pp.88 & 149.

20   PRO. CRES 34/211.

21   NYCRO. ZHP. Skelton Castle MSS.

22   Speight, H. *Romantic Richmondshire* (London: 1897) p.175. Gill, M.C. ''Yorkshire Smelting Mills. Part 1: The Northern Dales" *British Mining*, No.45 (1992), p.137.

23   Skelton Hall MSS. PRO. E134. 9 Will III. Trinity Term 18.

24   PRO. CRES 34/211.

THE MARRIOTT FAMILY (1660-1736)

After the execution of King Charles in 1649, all Crown property was confiscated by Parliament. A Parliamentary Commission, which sat at Richmond to value Crown lands prior to selling them off, ordered a survey to be made of the Grinton Mines in July 1650. The estimated annual value of the various mines was as follows:- Grinton £6, Harkerside £20, Whitaside £22 and Fremington £12. The mines remained unsold, however, probably because of uncertainty over the expected life of the Commonwealth.[1]

After the Restoration of Charles II, all the arrears and mesne profits from the mines were granted in 1660 to George Tushingham, who claimed they had been concealed from the Crown. He was a nominee for Reginald Marriott, Auditor of Crown Land Revenues, who was ideally placed to discover a situation such as at Grinton where no lease was granted for the mines after the Restoration, but, because of his position, was unable to apply directly for a lease.[2]

Tushingham does not appear to have asserted any ownership of the mines at Grinton, however, and the field was worked without a lease from the Crown by two local families. The Swales of Swale Hall and South Stainley worked Harkerside and Whitaside, and the Hillarys of Grinton worked on Grinton Moor.[3]

The Swale family had been at Grinton since 1157 when Alured de Swale, Chief Chamberlain to Walter de Gant, built a house on the site of Swale Hall. In 1650 the Hall, although described as nearly derelict, was confiscated by a Parliamentary Commission because the then-owner, Solomon Swale, was unable to pay fines for being a Catholic. Old Solomon, as he was known, had been working the mines at Harkerside apparently undisturbed for quite some time prior to 1649 but, owing to lack of capital, had been unable to work them properly. The Hall was purchased and rebuilt by a relative, another Solomon Swale, who also owned the manor of South Stainley, near Ripon. A barrister of Grays Inn, this Swale also a known Catholic and staunch Royalist.[4]

Despite his religious beliefs and his support for the Stuart cause, Swale survived the Interregnum and, when elected M.P. for Aldburgh in 1660, proposed the Restoration of the Monarchy in the House of Commons. The King rewarded him with a baronetcy and a grant of £2000 to compensate him for his suffering. He became High Sheriff of Yorkshire in 1670. Sir Solomon became a victim of the Titus Oates conspiracy in 1678 when he was expelled from the Commons as a convicted recusant and imprisoned in the King's Bench Prison. Whether he was one of those executed is not known, but he died in the same year.[5] He was succeeded by his son, Sir Henry Swale, and, when he died in 1682, Swale Hall and the family estates at South Stainley passed to his eldest son, the second Sir Solomon.

In 1692 this Sir Solomon leased the Harkerside mines to Phillip Bickerstaffe of Chirton, Northumberland, and Charles Middleton and Thomas Ellerker of London for a period of 31 years at a duty of 1/10th. Sir Solomon and these three partners were also to put up £20 each as capital stock to finance the "*Works*". The following year Ellerker died and his wife was appointed his executrix. The partners applied to her for her late husband's share of the costs which came to £50. Sir Solomon offered to take over her share in the partnership and paid £50 into the fund, but the widow and the other partners refused to assign Ellerker's share to Swale. The dispute was taken to court by Swale in 1695, but the outcome is unknown. Most likely the partnership was dissolved.[6]

THE FIRST CROWN MINERAL RIGHTS DISPUTE

This action brought the mines to the attention of Reginald Marriott, who noticed that no lease had been granted since the Restoration.[7] Once again acting through George Tushingham, he applied for a lease of the Grinton and Fremington mines. In July 1696 Samuel Travers, the Surveyor General, was ordered by the Lords of the Treasury to issue a new lease to start on the 18th August for a term of 31 years at the usual annual rent of 20 shillings, plus 1/10th duty. The *"Fine"* which was usually paid at the start of a new lease was waived and a clause inserted in the lease which stipulated that Marriott was to assert and defend the Crown title to the mines at his own expense. He was expressly forbidden to enter into a combination with any other pretended owners to the detriment of the Crown. The reason for this clause was to emerge very soon after the lease was granted and it is likely that the Treasury Lords were uncertain of the Crown title. Tushingham was ordered to render an account of all the mesne profits he had received since 1660 and pay the Crown 1/10th part of them.[8]

THE DISPUTE BETWEEN SIR SOLOMON SWALE AND ROGER HILLARY

The fears of the Treasury Lords about the Crown title to the Grinton mines were not unfounded for, late in 1696, the opening move for control of the mines came when Sir Solomon Swale served an order of ejectment against Roger Hillary. When the case came to Court, Roger Hillary stated in his defence that his grandfather had purchased the wastes and other lands from Henry Simpson in 1622 and this, therefore, gave him title to the minerals beneath the soil. His family had worked the coal mines on Grinton Moor since 1622 without interruption and for the past six years he had been working the lead mines on Grinton How and getting large quantities of ore.[9]

Sir Solomon counter-claimed that the mines were part of his manor of West Grinton. The Court declared that Hillary's claim to the lead mines beneath the soil was invalid as they were reserved to the Crown in the original sale in 1599, but his title of ownership of the wastes and coal mines was upheld. After the case was decided Swale was ordered to account to the Crown for the profits from the mines during his alleged usurpation.

[Footnote: During a lawsuit in 1890, legal opinion on the Hillary family's ownership of the unenclosed lands differed from the view taken by the Court at this time. In the original grant by Simpson to Robert Hillary in 1622, there was no mention of Manorial Title, wastes, mines or quarries. The Inquisition Post Mortem, taken after the death of Robert Hillary, and succeeding family documents make no mention of these rights until 1683, when the marriage settlement between Josiah Hillary and Mary Dawson included the wastes, mines and quarries. It was the opinion of the 1890s legal council that the title had been expanded at this time in order to obtain possession of the wastes which the Crown Officers appear to have overlooked.[10]]

REGINALD MARRIOTT'S DISPUTE WITH SIR SOLOMON SWALE

Marriott now had to obtain possession of the Harkerside and Whitaside mines from Swale, who claimed they were part of his reputed manor of "West Grinton". An Interlocutory order was made in Hilary Term 1696 ordering that, as the mines were leased by the Crown, Tushingham's lessee, John Ozell, should be named as Relator. An action of trespass and ejectment was then taken out by Ozell in the Exchequer of Pleas against Sir Solomon Swale to obtain possession of 10 mines at Harkerside and Whitaside. The case was heard at the York Assizes and found in Ozell's favour.

This verdict was contended by Sir Solomon Swale, who then brought in a cross action of ejectment in the name of his lessee, Clement Oldfield, against Tushingham in the Court of Chancery. He obtained a Fine at the Bar of the Exchequer of Pleas and the case was heard by the Lord Keeper, the Crown being represented by the Attorney General, Sir Thomas Trevor.[11]

Depositions were taken at Mary Douglas's house at Fremington in June 1697. Statements made by several of the miners, who had worked for Humphrey Wharton when he was lessee of the Grinton mines, confirmed that the mines now worked by Swale at Harkerside, Whitaside and Greenhills had been subleased by Wharton to George Carter, James Crathorne and Clement Chamber.[12]

Sir Solomon Swale, who fought the case himself, based his claim to the wastes of Harkerside and Whitaside on a Deed of Grant which, he alleged, had been made by Walter de Gant to his nephew and Chamberlain, Alured de Swale, in 1157. He claimed to possess the original copy of this document, but it was later discovered to be a forgery.[13] He also exhibited his father's marriage settlement of 1663 and two mortgages he had taken in 1688 and 1690, all of which had included the manor of West Grinton.[14]

The case was not as clear cut as it might seem, for Marriott must have been aware of the lease of 1692 and yet did nothing about it till 1697 when he was forced to defend the Crown title to all the Grinton mines. As Sir Solomon's grandfather had been the person who instigated the restoration of the Monarchy, it must have been particularly galling for him to have to fight the Crown in this case.

The Court decided that the earlier working by Humphrey Wharton was sufficient proof of Crown title and found against Swale.[15] The Court did, however, order Marriott to purchase from Swale the wastes from shafts which had been worked by him prior to the lawsuits being brought.[16]

This was the first of two complex legal actions in which Marriott sought to establish and defend the Crown's title to the Grinton mines. The outcome of the case benefited the Crown, but Marriott was bound by the terms of the lease to maintain its title at his own expense, in this case upwards of £2000. This may seem a large sum to lay out in order to defend a lessor's title, but it gives some idea of the profits he hoped to make from the mines.

Reginald Marriott died soon after this case and was succeeded by his son, also called Reginald. He was M.P. for Weymouth and married Dorothy, daughter of Thomas Pulleine of Carleton Hall, Master of the Stud to William III and High Sheriff of Yorkshire, in 1696.[17] In the 1720s he became a major shareholder in the Governor & Company of Copper Mines in the Principality of Wales.[18]

Early in 1705, Sir Solomon Swale made another attempt to recover the Harkerside and Whitaside mines when he filed another Bill with the Attorney General. Matters were further complicated when, in the following year, Thomas, the fifth Lord Wharton and owner of the neighbouring manor of Healaugh, claimed Harkerside and Grinton Moor as belonging to his manor. Two separate lawsuits ensued from these claims. The first was Marriott v Swale and the second was a Bill by Wharton against Marriott, Swale and Hillary. Both cases were set to be heard in Hillary Term 1707/8.[19]

LORD WHARTON'S TRESPASS
Thomas, the first Lord Wharton, received a grant of the manor of Muker and part of the manor of Healaugh in 1544 when he was appointed Warden of the Western Marches. The remainder of the manor of Healaugh had been purchased by Phillip, the fourth Lord Wharton, in 1653 from Sir Thomas Vachell and John Molineaux.[20] Vachell's share of the manor had included several parcels of ground in the enclosed lands at Harkerside and Wharton might have been trying to use these as a lever to get hold of the rest of this area, which included the wastes. Wharton had just finished a long legal wrangle with the owners of the Arkengarthdale mines in which he had tried to obtain possession of some of their richest mines and in which he had used the same confrontational tactics as he was to use in this dispute.[21]

In September 1705 Thomas, the fifth Lord Wharton, set the tone for the dispute by ordering his workmen to sink a shaft adjacent to one where Marriott's miners were working on Grinton How. Wharton's men also removed waste from these and other shafts which had been worked by Solomon Swale previous to 1697.[22] In an effort to stop them, Marriott applied for a mandate for peaceful possession. Two Barons of the Court of Exchequer ordered the issue of the Mandate in October 1705 and addressed it to Thomas, Lord Wharton, Solomon Swale and others, on penalty of a £1000 fine.[23]

Injunctions were served on several of Wharton's miners and agents in April 1706 by Mathew Sissons of Ripon, but Wharton's men ignored them and continued working. They dammed trenches cut by Marriott's men to direct water for washing ore and even took over and finished building a smithy on Grinton How and used it for sharpening their tools. Wharton's men then began sinking three shafts on the principal veins, but only succeeded in cutting into great springs of water, with the result that they drowned all the working shafts on the How.

Further injunctions were served in May 1706, but the men merely replied that they "cared not a fig for the injunctions". Even more drastic proof of the miners' contempt for the law occurred when Sissons tried to serve an injunction on

Thornton, who was the field smith. Unable to find him, Sissons and his party were about to leave Thornton's house when they were shot at with a fowling piece by John Sheldon, one of the miners, who then chased them as far as Harkerside.[24]

The foreman of the jury appointed to try the case when it came to Court in London was John Blackburn of Marrick, who was a partner in the Cupola Smelt Mill where Marriott had been sending his ore for smelting. Some days prior to the case being heard, he had a visit from Marriott's father-in-law, Thomas Pulleine, who offered to purchase Blackburn's debt-encumbered Marrick estate for £2300, providing he swayed the jury in Marriott's favour. Pulleine then visited Reuben Orton, another partner in the Cupola Mill, and offered to purchase the Mill for £400. Lord Wharton had also been busy, for he offered Blackburn a post at the Customs House in Liverpool.[25]

Prior to the case being heard in London, the jury met at Richmond in April 1708 and were shown a survey made jointly by John Hutchinson, acting for Marriott, and Leonard Brackenbury, for Wharton, to illustrate the case. After this, they proceeded to Harkerside to view the ground. Each member of the jury was paid five guineas on top of his travelling expenses. The trial itself took place in London on May 28th before a jury composed of Yorkshire gentry who heard evidence taken from 130 witnesses. Wharton's main evidence consisted of a copy of a Perambulation of the manor of Healaugh made by his tenants which had included the How mines and Harkerside.[26]

The decision of the Court was that the two manors were divided by the River Swale and, therefore, Wharton had no claim on lands lying to the south. Sir Walter Calverley, one of the jurors, noted in his diary that, after the case was found for Marriott: *"we had a handsome treat given us by Mr Marriott at the Rose, without Temple Bar, as also 20 guineays in a paper presented to each juryman"*.[27] Wharton applied for a retrial in Easter Term 1708/9, but, after various postponements, it seems to have fizzled out and no trial records for this attempt have survived.

After the case was found in his favour, Marriott reneged on the offer for the Marrick estate, but the purchase of the Cupola mill did go through. The unfortunate Blackburn, however, received none of the £400 from Orton.[28]

Sir Solomon Swale's case was the next to be dealt with. In this claim, he laid greater stress on the history of the lands granted to Bridlington Priory. In his defence, he maintained that the Crown's title was unfounded as the manor of Grinton was not a real manor at all. The title of manor only came into existence after the dissolution of Bridlington Priory when ministers of the Crown had referred to it as such. His manor of West Grinton was the real one. Even as early as 1613, a Recovery had been enrolled in the Feet of Fines to establish the manor of West Grinton. Indeed, his claim was not too far fetched, as the church and rectory were always referred to as the rectory of East Grinton.[29]

Once again Swale was defeated, but he did not give up all hope of establishing his title. In a letter written in September 1726 to Mathew Smales of Gilling, a prominent lawyer and land agent in the area, he expressed hopes that he might yet be successful. In a postscript to the letter, he said that Marriott was to be tried at the Old Bailey for wilful perjury. He ended with the words: *"if the jury find him guilty as I am confident they will the proof being full you will see me in possession of the lead mines before Michaelmass Day come twelve month and Marriott all torn to pieces"*.[30] Unfortunately, his hopes did not to come to fruition and he eventually died, ruined and brokenhearted, in December 1733 after spending time in the King's Bench Prison for debt, mainly incurred by trying to prove the existence of his reputed manor of West Grinton.[31]

MARRIOTT'S PEACEFUL TENURE

As soon as the Crown's title was secure, Marriott set about developing his mines, mainly on Grinton Moor and the How, from a series of shafts spread across the How veins. From the accounts covering the period of Marriott's tenure, we can build up a picture of the running of the mines. The Barmaster was Roger Bayne at a salary of £10 a year. This is the first documented reference to a Barmaster in the Swaledale area. The purser was William Bodinson at a salary of £20 p.a., and these two men also acted as Collectors of the King's Rents. Ralph Slack was the *"servicer and orderer of the works"* at a salary of £15 p.a. and his deputy, at £5 p.a., was Luke Yarker.

The returns show that Marriott was recouping his legal expenses rather slowly at first. From July 1697, when he first obtained full possession, to the end of 1698 the whole produce of the mines amounted to £2948 3s 10d, but, after expenses of £2434 7s 0d, his profit only came to £462 9s 1d. The working expenses continued to be a heavy drain on profits, which peaked at £4414 2s 6d in 1706, and from 1709 onwards went into rapid decline, apart from a surge in 1721 to 1723.[32]

Marriott had no smelt mill at Grinton then because the first lessees had smelted at their own mills at Clints and Gilling. The bulk of Marriott's ore was, therefore, sent for smelting in the *"fire hearths"* of the Marquis and Duke of Bolton at Marrick. When the Cupola Mill, also in Marrick, opened in 1702, enough ore was sent there to produce 1491 pigs. Smelting his ore at Marrick was a costly business, however. For example, in 1703 carriage ore alone cost £172 19s 4d and smelting charges added another £151 18s 6d. It must have become very clear that it would be much cheaper to build his own mill, if he was going to have to pay out sums like this every year.

The actual date for the building of the first smelt mill at Grinton is not known, but, from two purchases of land made by Marriott, a possible date can be inferred. In order to erect his own mill, Marriott had first of all to gain possession to the surface rights of the unenclosed land at Grinton which belonged to the Hillary family. In December 1705, using two nominees Bateman and Budgett, he purchased for £893 6s 8d several houses and large parcels of land in Grinton together with one third of the manorial title from John Hillary. In January 1710

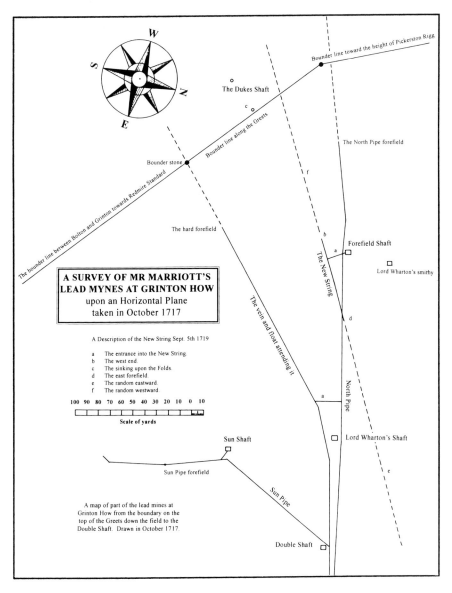

A SURVEY OF MR MARRIOTT'S
LEAD MYNES AT GRINTON HOW
upon an Horizontal Plane
taken in October 1717

The Dukes Shaft

Bounder line toward the height of Pickerston Rigg

Bounder line along the Greets

Bounder stone

The bounder line between Bolton and Grinton towards Redmire Standard

The hard forefield

The North Pipe forefield

Forefield Shaft

Lord Wharton's smithy

The New String

The vein and float attending it

North Pipe

A Description of the New String Sept. 5th 1719

a   The entrance into the New String.
b   The west end.
c   The sinking upon the Folds.
d   The east forefield.
e   The random eastward.
f   The random westward.

100 90 80 70 60 50 40 30 20 10 0 10

Scale of yards

Sun Shaft

Sun Pipe forefield

Sun Pipe

Lord Wharton's Shaft

A map of part of the lead mines at
Grinton How from the boundary on the
top of the Greets down the field to the
Double Shaft. Drawn in October 1717.

Double Shaft

Fig.2

21

he purchased the other two thirds of the wastes from Samuel Hillary for £200. To accomplish this, he had once more used the two nominees, Bateman and Budgett, who in turn were acting for Marriott's two sons, James and Richard.[33]

Included in the two sales were the wastes, turbary rights and mines of coal and stone. This put Marriott in a position to build his own mill and a probable date could be soon after the second purchase. (The mill is dealt with more fully in a later chapter as to develop the sequence here would result in too much confusion.)

In July 1720 Marriott presented a petition for an extension of the lease, which was due to expire in 1727, in which he stated that the mines had been in "*decay*" for several years and that he had incurred great expense in improving them.[34] The accounts for the previous four years do show a loss, which could well have been incurred in development and exploration work, as the shafts which produced the high returns at the beginning of the lease began to decline. A reversionary lease was granted by the Treasury Lords to start on August 28th for a further 23 years at the usual yearly rental of 20 shillings, with the duty reduced to 1/8th.[35]

Reginald Marriott died in April 1730 and the mine lease and manorial title passed to his son, Hugh.[36] Production at the mines had declined steadily. From 1728 they had been worked at a loss and in 1730 no lead was sold. Clearly mindful of the situation, Hugh Marriott cast about for prospective buyers for the manor and the remainder of the term of the Crown lease.

In August 1733, the Court of the London Lead Company was informed that Hugh Marriott was prepared to sell his manorial title, the mine lease, the smelt mill with utensils, and a burgage house in Richmond for £2800. By the 11th of September, the two parties had prepared a memorandum, agreeing that the sale should go ahead at a reduced purchase price of £2625 and Marriott was paid two guineas as part of the purchase money. On September 18th 1733, Marriott was sent a letter informing him that an examination of his title was to be made. The last reference which occurs in the minute books of the London Lead Company to the sale mentions that a committee was to be set up to consider the sale after the title had been examined. No more is heard regarding the sale. The solicitor who examined the title would have soon discovered that Marriott, as lessee from the Crown, had no right to sell the lease.[37]

REFERENCES

1 PRO. CRES 34/211. File 1441. PRO. E317/26.

2 DRO. D/HH/6/4/1. Fieldhouse, R. & Jennings, B. *A History of Richmond & Swaledale* (London: Phillimore, 1978) p.201.

3 Harrison, P. *History of the Wapentake of Gilling West* (London, 1885). p.233. Raistrick & Jennings, p.157.

4 Harrison, P. p.235/8.

5 Bean, W.W. *Parliamentary Representation of Six Northern Counties* (Hull: 1890) p.737.

6 Harrison, p.239/240.

7 PRO. CRES 3/85.

8 PRO. E367/3645. PFF 5045. PRO. CRES 34/211. Copy of lease in Marrick Priory MSS. Brotherton Library. Leeds.

9 PRO. CRES 34/211. Harrison. P. p.233/4. PRO. Exchequer depositions. E134 9 Will III. Trin 18. DRO D/HH/6/4/1.

10 Barker MSS. Charlesworth v Broderick.

11 PRO. CRES 34/211. NYCRO ZHP. Raistrick & Jennings p.157.

12 PRO. Exchequer Depositions. E134. 9 Will III. Trin 18.

13 Clay C.T. (Ed.) *Early Yorkshire Charters, Vol.5: Honour of Richmond* (Yorkshire Record Society, 1936), p.342.

14 NYCRO. Cront Horn.

15 DRO. D/HH/6/4/1.

16 YML. Hailstone MSS. Box 5. File 41.

17 Burke, J.B. *Dictionary of Landed Gentry* (London: Harrison, 1898) p.1222.

18 Scott, W.R. *The Constitution and Finance of English, Scottish and Irish Joint Stock Companies to 1720* (Selden Society, 1910-11) pp.443-445. PRO Chancery depositions. C12/1495/1. Raistrick & Jennings, p.157.

19 PRO. CRES 34/211. File 1441. Harrison. p.241.

20 VCH Healaugh, p.241.

21 Tyson, L.O. *A History of the Manor and Lead Mines of Arkengarthdale, Yorkshire* (Sheffield: NMRS, British Mining No.29, 1986) pp.16-19.

22 YML. Hailstone MSS. Box 5. File 41.

23 NYCRO. Cront 1. Peacock.

24 YML. Hailstone MSS. Box 5. File 41.

25 Tyson, L.O. *A History of the Manor and Lead Mines of Marrick, Yorkshire* (Sheffield: NMRS, British Mining No.38, 1989) pp.30f. BL. Marrick Priory MSS. DRO. D/HH/6/4/139. Raistrick & Jennings. p.157.

26 Barker, J.L. "Document relating to dispute over ownership of Grinton Manor" *Memoirs of the NCMRS* (December 1967), pp.26-30.

27 Memorandum Book of Sir Walter Calverley, Bart, Surtees Society, 1886, pp.118/119.

28 Tyson. L.O. *Marrick*, 1989, p.31. BL. MP MSS.

29 PRO. CRES 34/211. File 1441. Harrison. p.241.

30 YML. Hailstone. Box 4. File 7.

31 Harrison, p.237. Bean, pp.237 & 737.

32 PRO. LRRO 3/85.

33 PRO. CRES 2/1390. Barker MSS. Charlesworth v Broderick.

34 PRO. Calendar of Treasury Papers.

35 PRO. CRES 2/1390. NYCRO. ZHP. Mic 1324.

36 YML. Hailstone. Box 4. File 41.

37 NRO. London Lead Co Minute Books. LLC/7, pp.143-148. Tyson, L.O. & Gill, M.C. "The London Lead Company's Yorkshire Mines: A New Assessment" *British Mining*, No.45 (1992), pp.151-161.

THE MOORE FAMILY (1736-1765)

EDMUND MOORE 1736-1752

When negotiations with the London Lead Company fell through, the lease was demised to Edmund Moore of Redruth in 1736 for an annual rent of £100, which was later reduced to £21. The smelt mill was not included in the sale.[1] Edmund Moore held shares in a number of mines in the Redruth area, including Wheal Fortune, Halleage and Wheal Radnor. He was also a major shareholder in 1728 with Reginald Marriott in the Governor & Company of Copper Mines in the Principality of Wales.[2]

In June 1743 Moore presented a petition applying for a reversionary lease of the mines. In this petition, he claims to have expended large sums of money making trials and was close to discovering *"what the miners call an Undersett to the Old Vein which lies considerably deeper than that formerly worked"*. The report to the Crown Commissioners recommended that Moore be encouraged, since he paid his rent, kept accounts well and had lost money prospecting. The term desired was for twenty three and a half years, computed from 28th August 1750. A warrant for the lease was issued by the Commissioners on the 22nd of June 1743. It was noted in the lease that the lessee had the right to erect mills.[3]

When the Letters Patent were issued, they included, as usual, the Fremington Mines. When Moore attempted to start work there, however, he was opposed by William Wharton, who then began an action against the Attorney General who represented the Crown on Moore's behalf. He maintained that, as his family had also been paying the rent since the lease of Fremington mines was first granted to them, he had full right to them. Marriott had also paid this rent, but had never obtained possession. The Crown appears to have solved the case amicably and in 1750 Moore granted a moiety of them to Mr Chambers and Mr Keys who were to bear one half of the costs. (This episode will be dealt with more fully in the section devoted to the Fremington mines.)[4]

Moore extended his mining interests outside the Swaledale area in 1751. In partnership with Slingsby Bethell, he took a 21 year lease of land and copper mines at Middleton Tyas, owned by James Shuttleworth of Forcett Park. Soon after taking this lease, his workmen and agent, Thomas Rosewarne, were involved in a disagreement with the neighbouring Derbyshire miners over drainage of their mine and threats were made to blow up each other's workings with gunpowder.[5]

MRS FRANCES MOORE 1752-1765

Edmund Moore died in January 1752 and his estate and mine shares in Cornwall and Yorkshire were divided into three parts. One third went to his wife, Mrs Frances Moore, one third to his cousin, Anthony Johns, and the other third to John Bohemia of Redruth. Mrs Moore seems to have been the partner most concerned with running the mines, as the agent, Thomas Rosewarne, addressed all his communications to her.[6]

Lydia Marriott, who had title to the manor of Grinton from her late husband Hugh, the son and heir of Reginald Marriott, sold the manor in May 1756 to Alderman Caleb Readshaw of Richmond. This sale brought to an end the Marriott involvement with Grinton which began nearly 100 years earlier. Included in the sale was the smelting mill with a little house or chamber, and all the smiths' cottages and sheds on the mines which had been in the tenure of the Moores.[7]

The Readshaw family were prominent merchants in Richmond where, in the early 1700s, Caleb's grandfather had established the lucrative trade of exporting knitted yarn stockings and woollen night caps to the Netherlands.[8] This work was put out to the families of miners and farmers in the Dales and provided a useful supplementary source of income. The miners themselves would often knit as they walked to and from work.[9] The Readshaws were also involved with the copper mines near Richmond and lead mining ventures in other parts of Swaledale and Wharfedale.[10] A relative of the family, Robert Readshaw, had been appointed agent for the London Lead Company's mines in Scotland in 1733. On his recommendation Caleb's brothers, Cuthbert and John Readshaw, had become partners in the Craigtown Mining Company which was formed in 1764 to work the lead mines at Blackcraig and Machermore in Minnigaff, Galloway.[11]

Fortunately Thomas Rosewarne's Bargain Book for the Grinton Mines covering the period from 1758 to 1762 has survived and this gives some idea of the working practices at the time. The mines were let out to various partnerships which tended to consist of the same people with each person taking a new bargain in their name as principal partner. As a result, the whole field was run by this one group of people.[12]

The first group of mines subleased by Rosewarne in March 1758 were on Grinton How and concentrated around the North and Sun (south) Rakes. Each partnership was allowed four meers of ground, a meer being 30 yards in length. There was no stipulation of quartercord at these shafts in 1758, but by 1762 it was inserted in the leases and became established as custom of the field. Low Cow Shaft was the principal shaft on the Sun Rake, and the North Rake was worked from the Whim Shaft where the ground was let as far as Lord Wharton's Shaft. The bargains were for a period of four years, paying a duty of 1/5th, and Mrs Moore also received all slag lead after smelting.

To smelt her ore, Mrs Moore rented the How Smelt Mill from Caleb Readshaw. Her lessees paid three shillings per fodder for smelting their ore there and they were also responsible for dressing it ready for smelting and carrying it to the smelt mill. Readshaw provided peat, and also coal from the Grinton Moor Colliery for use in the hearth at the mill.

In October 1759 a dispute arose with Caleb Readshaw over the price paid for smelting the first year's ore production. An agreement between Cuthbert Readshaw, acting for his nephew Caleb, and Thomas Rosewarne decided that the case should go to arbitration. As the How Smelt Mill was retained as belonging to the manor and always excepted from the Crown leases, there was always a potential source of friction if the Lord of the Manor was not actually involved with the mines.

James Simpson of Reeth and John Summers of Grassington were appointed as arbitrators in the dispute. Summers was a Swaledale man who had moved to Grassington where he was partner with, and agent for, Readshaw in a number of mines.[13] They found that 194 fodders of lead had been smelted at the mill between August 1758 and September 1759. It was decided that, for the following year, all ore smelted at the mill would be paid for at the same price as the previous year.[14]

An Account of the lead produced at the Grinton How Mines
from August 25th 1758 to September 30th 1759.
Smelted at the How Smelting Mill.

	Pieces
Anthony Cradock senior at the Whim Shaft	400
Tobias Cradock at the Whim Shaft	85
To Mr James Simpson at the Whim Shaft	71
To Anthony Cradock junior at the Whim Shaft	19
To Mr John Alderson at Cow Shaft	255
To James Simpson & Co at the High Ventilator	2500
James Simpson & Co at the Low Ventilator	200
To the How Hush	26
To the Harker Hush	91
To Robert Elliott & Co at Harker Hush	53
To Richard Lonsdale at Green Hills	46
To Jane Lonsdale the Mill Slags	33
To Miles Hall - Slags	10
To Thomas Dunn & James Robinson - How Waste	14

which makes 194 fodder or 9 Marks and 12 fodder.

The money received by Mr Thomas Rosewarne of the above said Cradock's and Mr Readshaw's peats they made of to Smelt their ore was £1 19s 0d.

EXPANSION OF THE MINES

Mining activity had tended to concentrate on the Grinton Moor Mines till 1761 when ground to the west was partitioned out to various groups of Adventurers. Since 1728 the mines had operated largely at a loss, only making a profit on five occasions. After this date, however, there was a massive rise in production as these new areas were developed.

In June 1761 Rosewarne granted a lease of ground at Whitaside, east of Greenhills Mine, to John Harker and partners for the remainder of the term that the Crown lease had left to run. John Harker and Adam Bird had a 1/4th share, whilst 1/8th shares were held by Robert Elliott, Thomas Stodart and Christopher Raine. Mrs

Moore had also taken a 1/8th share and she was to receive 1/6th duty on lead from the ore hearth and the slag hearth.

The area between the How and Harkerside in which the Grove Beck Mines were to be developed was let in September 1761 to Thomas Dun and 10 partners, one of whom was Thomas Rosewarne with a 1/8th share. The partners were to *"chase"* 20 meers of ground, each meer consisting of 30 yards. When they had done this, they were to pay Mrs Moore a duty of 1/5th on all lead smelted from the ore they found until 20 fodders of lead had been made. They were then to *"chase"* the ground again and, when 20 fodders had been made from this ore, Mrs Moore would pay them *"20 Guinease"*. Permission for hushing was granted, but it had to be carried out between the 29th of September and the last day of March. This would ensure that an adequate supply of water was available for dressing during the summer months.

The Harkerside area was leased in October 1761, at a duty of 1/5th, to Robert Elliott and partners to begin *"as far north as the level arse and as far south as Grove Beck head and as far east and west as the partners thought fit"*. The initial grant was to run for four years, during which time they were to work the Top Setts, and, if by the end of this term they had sunk a shaft to the Undersets, the lease would be extended as long as Mrs Moore's lease lasted. Mrs Moore was to have half of the slag smelted from their ore, a practice known as *"Pig and Pig"*.[15]

THE HARKER DISPUTE
By the end of 1761 Harker had sunk five shafts and, after putting out cross cuts from them, discovered a new vein in his ground at Whitaside. Hearing of this success, Richard Lonsdale, who had hushed an area a quarter of a mile from Harker's grant from 1758 to 1760, applied to Rosewarne in January 1762 for 10 meers of ground adjoining the east end of Harker's ground.[16]

In April Lonsdale began sinking a shaft in Harker's ground and in June began another, only eight yards from Cow Shaft, the main shaft in Harker's ground. Harker complained to Rosewarne who went to Lonsdale and showed him the bargain book with the agreement and ground granted to Harker which Lonsdale had made no objection to at the time of signing. Lonsdale, however, carried on work and in July Rosewarne issued a discharge and pulled down the jack-roll at the shaft top.

Lonsdale waited till September, then began sinking a shaft near Ashpot Gutter Head until discharged once again in October when the shaft head was thrown in. Lonsdale then seems to have transferred his shares and Henry Birkbeck took charge of the partnership. In April 1763 Birkbeck began working day and night at Ashpot Gutter with a large number of miners and, despite a discharge being given in May, continued working till he was stopped by a Court Injunction issued on February 9th 1764. During this period, he raised lead to the value of £500 and since February 1st carried 94 horse load valued at £60 away from the shaft top.[17]

During 1763 Harker had begun legal proceedings to stop Birkbeck & Co trespassing on his ground. The case Harker et al v Birkbeck et al was heard on June 11th 1764 at the York Assize. The Court decided in Harker's favour and one shilling damages were awarded, subject to a ruling, with the consent of both parties, that the verdict should be subject to the Court's opinion. If found for Harker, then he was at liberty to proceed with a charge of trespass, but if for the defendants, a nonsuit would be returned. The legal points of the case centred on two questions. These were:- (1) whether an action for trespass could be maintained and (2) whether the agreement between Rosewarne and Harker was admissible as evidence as it was not on stamped paper.

On the first point, argument centred on whether the actions of the defendants had been immediately or consequentially injurious to the plaintiffs. The Court decided in favour of the defendants, as their counsel had successfully argued that their actions had not injured the plaintiffs as they were not the owners of the surface rights but merely lessees. An act of trespass had taken place, but the injury was consequential, whereas Harker's counsel had argued the trespass was immediately damaging to his clients. The case, if brought by Mrs Moore rather than by Harker, would have been more successful as she was the owner of the surface rights.

On the second point, most of the argument centred on whether mining agreements, or take notes, signed on unstamped paper, as was the usual case, were legally binding in law. It was argued that a memorandum, or take note, was merely an agreement to work and not a lease, indenture or deed poll and, therefore, did not require to be on stamped paper but was indeed only legally binding upon the parties actually starting work. As the plaintiff, Harker, had been working the mine, the lease, therefore, was actuated and legally binding.[18]

Probably encouraged by the result of the case, Lonsdale filed a Supplemental Bill against Harker for trespass. He alleged that Rosewarne had colluded with Harker and predated Harker's agreement to the one he had taken out in 1762. The legal proceedings dragged on till 1765, by which time both Rosewarne and Mrs Moore were dead. In 1767 Harker's widow, Dorothy, and the other partners signed an agreement empowering Leonard Hartley of Middleton Tyas to obtain all the papers relating to the case from Thomas Cornforth of Richmond. Hartley was then to act as their attorney in conjunction with John Roper of Bedale, the attorney for Richard Lonsdale and partners, and reach a settlement. The court instructed Ralph Hutchinson, the agent for Whitaside, to pay Leonard Hartley 1/6th of their ore until the matter was finally resolved. The final outcome of this saga is unknown at present.[19]

REFERENCES

1 PRO. CRES 2/1390. DRO. D/HH/6/4/2. NYCRO. ZHP. Mic 1324.

2 PRO. Chancery Depositions. C12/1495/1.

3 NYCRO. ZHP. Mic 1324. PRO. CRES 2/1390.

4 PRO. CRES 34/211.

5 Hornshaw, T.R. *Copper Mining at Middleton Tyas* (Northallerton: NYCRO, Publication No.6, 1975) pp.14, 43, 112.

6 DRO. D/HH/6/4/2. PRO. Chancery Depositions. C12/1310/18.

7 Barker MSS. Charlesworth v Broderick.

8 Hatcher, C.J. "Richmond and District Civic Society" *The Richmond Review*, 1990, pp.31-33.

9 Hartley, M. & Ingilby, J. *The Old Hand Knitters of the Dales* (Clapham: Dalesman, 1951). Gill, M.C. "Mining and Proto-industrialisation" *British Mining*, No.41 (1990), pp.99-110.

10 Gill, M.C. *The Grassington Mines* (Keighley: British Mining No.46, 1993) pp.20, 46, 73. Clarkson. C. *History of Richmond* (1814) pp.324-6.

11 Donnachie, I. *Industrial Archaeology of Galloway* (Newton Abbot: David & Charles, 1971) pp.119-20. I am indebted to Bill Harvey for this information. NRO. London Lead Company Minute Book. LLC/7.

12 NYCRO. ZKU. 1X. 1/43.

13 Gill, *Grassington*, p.19.

14 NYCRO. ZHP. Mic 1324.

15 NYCRO. ZKU. 1X. 1/43.

16 PRO. Chancery Depositions. C12/20/2.

17 PRO. Chancery Depositions. C12/342/3. C12/20/2.

18 NYCRO. ZQH. Mic 1169. Sir James Burrow. Reports of Cases Adjudged in the Court of Kings Bench, Dublin, 1785. Harker et al v Birkbeck et al. pp.1556-1565.

19 NYCRO. ZQH. Mic 1169. ZKU. Mic 1597. Chancery Depositions. C12/44/36.

WILLIAM KNIGHTON (1765-1771)

Mrs Frances Moore died intestate in May 1765. Her niece and next of kin, Elizabeth Knighton, wife of William Knighton of Beerferris in Devon, had to take out Letters of Administration at York and Canterbury in order to inherit all her estate and mine shares. The other one-third shares were held by Anthony Johns, Jane, the daughter of John Bohemia, and her husband, William Hambly.[1] In February 1766 they agreed that William Knighton should petition the Lords of the Treasury for an extension of the lease, which was due to expire in March 1774.

The Crown Steward for the Grinton Mines submitted a report on the income derived from the mines beginning in September 1750, when Edmund Moore's lease had commenced, to 29th September 1763. This showed that for eight of those years the mines were worked at a loss to the lessees amounting to £740 7s 9d, while profits for the other six years amounted to only £849 13s 3d. Royalties paid to the Crown during this period amounted to £106 4s 1d.[2]

THE CHAUNCY TOWNSEND DISPUTE

The Lords Commissioners granted a warrant for the new lease, but for some unknown reason the filing of the warrant was delayed by the Clerk of the Pipe. The application was then challenged by Chauncy Townsend, lessee of the Duke of Bolton's neighbouring mines in Apedale. Townsend was an important mining venturer, at this time being involved with several lead mines in Cardiganshire, as well as coal mining ventures, copper smelting and refining works in South Wales.[3]

He had begun negotiating an arrangement with William Knighton's agents to bring water out of his mines through a level driven in from Grinton ground. The extent of the area to be granted and the terms on which it was to be financed were agreed in principle, subject to an inquiry as to whether it would be detrimental to Knighton's mines. When enquiries were made among Knighton's sublessees, it was soon realised that this level, if driven, would certainly drain the Apedale mines, but would in turn drown out the mines on the Grinton side, particularly those on Grinton Moor and Harkerside.

William Knighton broke off negotiations and Chauncy Townsend then petitioned the Lords Commissioners for a lease. In his claim he admitted that his mines were now waterlogged, which prevented further working of what was very rich ground. He offered to purchase the Grinton lease for the ridiculously high price of £3000 and give one half of the produce as Royalty instead of the 1/8th paid by Knighton, an indication of the extent of the profit Townsend hoped to gain from his mines in Castle Bolton and of the incredible lengths and expense he was prepared to go to to achieve this.

In affidavits taken from miners working the Grinton mines in July 1766 they expressed their concern about Townsend getting the lease. They pointed out that no one could afford to pay one half his profits and still make proper trials, and that he was unlikely to work the Grinton mines for half the profit when he could work his own for full profit.

John Harker, one of the miners interviewed, said that it could be argued that the profits to the Crown had been poor, owing to the manner in which the Crown lessees had sublet the ground. The various mines were leased to different sets of Adventurers, reserving 1/6th duty to the lessee, out of which the Crown received 1/8th. The remaining 5/6ths, out of which the Crown received no royalty, went to the Adventurers. There was, however, no other way of working the mines, owing to the uncertain nature of the ground, and no Adventurer would take a lease without the chance of a reasonable share of the profits. There were between 10 and 20 persons involved in each partnership, which made any losses easier to carry. The mines yielded £5000 or £6000 profit between 1774 and 1776. Although this was divided between the Crown, the lessees and the Adventurers, the Crown profit was still reasonable. Royalties to the Crown for the past 30 years had amounted to only £899, of which nearly £600 had been paid in the past two years.

To strengthen his claim, William Knighton submitted the evidence given by his sublessees as to the detrimental effect on the Crown's mines if Townsend obtained the lease. He maintained that the method now used to work the field was the best possible in the given circumstances, owing to the highly speculative nature of the operation. He also stated that in the past two years the vein had been found again and, in this time, the profits to the Crown amounted to £566, with good prospects for the future. He stressed that in the past the lessees had sustained large losses and still given the Crown a profit, albeit a small one, therefore, it was only right and proper that the Crown should show good faith and grant a Reversionary Lease.

Soon after Townsend presented his petition, and recognising that its success was unlikely, the Duke of Bolton applied for the lease. This was followed by applications from the Dukes of Grafton and Northumberland and Sir Lawrence Dundas. A reminder of the past came from another applicant, Peregrine Cust, the Speaker's brother, who laid claim to the mines and the whole manor of Grinton under Sir Solomon Swale's old cause. The Duke of Bolton then merged his claim with Townsend's, probably hoping that his name would influence the decision.

GEORGE JACKSON'S SURVEY
The Surveyor General rejected Townsend's petition on the grounds that it was unreasonable and improper. The granting of a new lease to Knighton was also delayed as the inquiry had demonstrated to the Lords Commissioners that their knowledge of the Grinton mines was severely lacking. Richard Herbert, the Surveyor General, was ordered to make a report on the state of the mines. He requested George Jackson of Richmond to make the first comprehensive survey of Grinton and draw a plan of the area.[4]

The report presented by Herbert in October 1768 clearly showed that the way in which the Crown lessees handled the field was biased towards the Adventurers and detrimental to Crown interests. The Crown lessees were accountable by the express wording of their grant for 1/8th of all the "*clear*" yearly profits. An examination of the returns, however, showed they were not adhering to these terms. Since 1761, it had become the practice to lease to Adventurers at 1/5th or

1/6th and, instead of accounting to the Crown for a full 1/8th, they had only accounted for 1/8th out of the reserved duties of 1/5th or 1/6th.[5]

Production figures from the four principal mines from 1761, when ore was found, to 1767 were presented to demonstrate the discrepancy:

	Fodder	Av. Price per fodder	£	s	d
Grovebeck Mine	1185.27	£15	17,779	10	00
Whitaside Mine	1844.23	£15	27,667	10	00
Fearnought Mine	1977	£15	29,655	00	00
12 Meers Mine	315.18	£15	4,731	00	00
Total lead raised	5321.68	Total value	79,833	00	00

	£	s	d
Disbursements made by Adventurers came to	40,724	12	10¾
Disbursements by lessees for 6 years comes to	2,271	19	09¼
Total Disbursements	42,996	12	08

	£	s	d
Clear profit arising from said mines for 6 years	36,836	07	04
The 1/8th clear profit should have been paid Crown	4,604	10	11

The residue would have been £3223 16s 5d which would have belonged to the Crown lessees and their sublessees. Instead, the lessees in their accounts with the Exchequer for the previous six years had paid £874 19s 7d, leaving a deficit of £3729 11s 0d. There was also ore lying on the bank which, according to George Jackson, was worth nearly £20,485. The Treasury Lords, obviously disturbed by Jackson's and Herbert's revelations, declined to grant the Reversionary lease requested by Knighton.

TROUBLE AT T'MILL

In 1770 Scott's Mill on Grovebeck became the scene of violent disorder when some of Lord Pomfret's miners attacked the mill. John Scott, the mill owner, was a shareholder in the Beldi Hill Mines which were the subject of a prolonged dispute between Lord Pomfret and Thomas Smith. Thomas Smith was using Scott's Mill till he was able to build his own at Beldi Hill.

James Peacock and nine other men were ordered to appear at the Quarter Sessions on April 19th 1771. It was alleged that *"with force and arms at Grinton, with gavelocks, pickaxes, shovels, hammers and pitchforks, they made a riotous assembly at the smelting mill in Grinton"*. They had blocked up the mill race and made a breach in the mill dam, causing the stoppage of the waterwheel used for the ore hearth bellows. The damage was repaired only to have Peacock repeat the same action twice more. After evidence had been given, they were fined one shilling each. Attacks took place at other mills owned by Pomfret and Smith with equal violence. Given that violence was used by both sides during the dispute, plus the fact that many of those involved had been dealt with before by the court, the lightness of the fine was quite justified.[6]

REFERENCES

1 PRO. Chancery Depositions. C12/1310/18.

2 DRO. D/HH/6/4/2. PRO. CRES 2/1390.

3 Rogers, K.H. *The Newcomen Engine in the West of England* (Bradford on Avon: Moonraker Press, 1976, p.48).

4 PRO. MPE 531. British Library MPE 390.

5 PRO. LRRO. 3/85.

6 Batty, M. *Bygone Reeth* (Reeth: Methodist Church Council, 1985) p.52.

THE KNIGHTON, READSHAW PARTNERSHIP (1771-1817)

Whilst Knighton had been involved with the Townsend affair, the other two share holders had begun legal proceedings in which they alleged that they had received no money from the mine leases as due to them under the terms of Edmund Moore's will. The case was heard in the latter part of 1768 and, despite the allegations of deception and mismanagement against William Knighton, the case was decided in his favour. After the case, Anthony Johns' share was purchased by Richard Turner of Tavistock, Knighton's attorney, and Caleb Readshaw, Lord of the Manor of Grinton, bought out the Hamblys' one-third share in December 1771.[1]

During the following two years, Readshaw demised his shares in his mining activities to various members of his family. The reason for these actions would become clearer during bankruptcy proceedings taken against him in 1791.[2]

A new lease for the Grinton and Fremington Mines was applied for by Readshaw, Knighton and Turner in 1774.[3] In their application, they asked for a reduction of the duty from 1/5th to 1/8th, owing to the poor state of the mines. Peter Burrell, the Surveyor General, ordered George Jackson to make a new survey of the mines in November of the same year. The survey, presented in April 1775, showed that mining activities were practically non-existent.

Harkerside Mine had been leased on the 10th of February 1774 to James Stoddart & Company. The duty to the Crown lessees was 1/5th, plus a further duty of 15 shillings per fodder for the residue after the 1/5th had been removed. About £40 had been spent on trials and not more than £20 raised in ore. Twenty people were employed at the mine and the ore raised would just about cover the working costs.

The Grovebeck Mines were leased on June 18th 1774 to Fowler, Hickes & Co. for 21 years at the same duty as Harkerside. They had spent about £300 on fresh trials, and about 30 men, women and children were employed above and below ground. The ore raised was barely paying expenses.

Whitaside Mine was let to Thomas Simpson & Co. in June, also for the same duty. This duty was to be reduced if the petition for a reduction of the Crown lessees' duty was accepted. There was also a further duty of 12s 6d per fodder to be paid on the residue of lead after the 1/5th had been taken out. A barrier of 20 yards was to be left between Whitaside and the Duke of Bolton's liberty. Here they had spent about £700 on trials and raised only £300 worth of ore. There were about 80 people employed at the mine and production was described as indifferent, scarcely paying expenses. The Crown lessees had themselves spent about £80 on trials at Devis and Sharrow Hill which were unsuccessful.

Working from the Account Books of George Conmer, the field agent, it was found that, between September 17th 1772 and March 12th 1774, a total of 271 tons of ore had been raised at Whitaside and that no ore had been raised at any other part of the field.

Extract from George Jackson's Survey of 1775.
In order to prove the truth of the calculations made by the said lessees and subjoined to their petition I have as below stated from the ore and lead book kept by George Conmer, the Field Agent, an exact account of all the ore raised on Whitaside, with the produce thereof in lead, from 17/09/ 1772 to 12/03/1774 during which time no ore was raised in any other part of the premises. 24 stones per horse.

ORE RAISED				PRODUCE IN LEAD						
Horse	Stone	Mark	Pcs	Fdr	H	Q	Lb	Horse	Sto	lbs
2284	8	WPS	2082	124	6	2	0	18	9	0
555	12	1773	784	46	5	2	21	12	0	0
634	8	FN:HCO	459	27	1	1	0	23	10	0
861	16	1773	466	27	19	0	32	30	22	0
289	18	1774	352	21	8	3	21	13	12	12
4625	14		4143	246	19	2	18	98	6	12

This divided by 5 leaves the horse in fodder.
Average weight per piece = 146.84 lbs.
Total lead 271.58 tons

Caleb Readshaw then opposed the other two partners and applied to the Commissioners for a lease to be granted in his name only. The parties, however, compromised and, upon a payment of £500 to Readshaw, the lease was taken in his name with Knighton and Turner holding a one-third share each. The new lease of the Grinton and Fremington mines was for a term of 31 years from December 3rd 1776. The request for a reduced duty to 1/5th was rejected, but the Commissioners did accept Jackson's recommendation of 1/7th. This new lease contained several special covenants securing the due rendering of the Crown's reserved share of all production from the mines. These covenants ensured that the Crown would receive the 1/7th Duty from the sub-lessees as well as from the Crown lessees.[4]

In order to ensure the Crown lessees conformed with the special covenants in the new lease, John Hutchinson of Redmire was appointed Crown Agent for the Grinton Mines in May 1786 by Jeremiah Robinson, Receiver of Land Revenue for the County of York. Hutchinson was paid 2s 6d in the pound as wages from the produce of duty lead received from the lessees and sold by him. He was succeeded by his son, George, in this post and then, on George's death in 1813, the post went to George Emmerson of Reeth.[5]

SUMMER LODGE - A NEW MINE AND A NEW DISPUTE

George Jackson's survey showed that two new mines had been started in the Summer Lodge area at the western extremity of the field, an area which up till this time had been untested. Previous Crown lessees had probably ignored the Summer Lodge area because they were getting sufficient production from their Grinton Mines. This situation changed, however, when a very rich vein was discovered at the neighbouring Spout Gill Mines, owned by the Earl of Pomfret. These mines were being worked by the Parke brothers whose agent was Joseph Cowling. He had previously worked for Mrs Moore's agent, Rosewarne, at Middleton Tyas and later acted for the Parkes' interests there when they were in partnership with Leonard Hartley, who later became William Knighton's agent at Grinton.[6]

Cowling now set out to take advantage of his knowledge gained as agent for the Spout Gill mines and to set up as a mine adventurer in his own right. Fully aware that the Stotter Gill and Crackpot Moor Veins must extend into Grinton, he and his brother, Thomas, applied for and were granted Take Notes in February 1774 to make trials in the Summer Lodge area adjoining Spout Gill.[7]

Thomas Cowling & Co were granted 10 Meers of ground at 30 yards per meer in February 1774 at the usual terms of 1/5th duty and a further duty of 15 shillings per fodder after the 1/5th was paid. This ground was in the area to the east of Summer Lodge Tarn. They had spent about £40 on trials when, in the October, a *"discovery"* was made. This was to become known as Summer Lodge Vein.

Another eight meers of ground had also been let in February to Joseph Cowling, George Jackson and Fowler Hickes in an area below the tarn, near Rowntree Hole. About £10 was spent sinking two trial shafts which found an extension of Crackpot Moor Vein, which was named Cowling Rake. With typical Swaledale humour, one of these shafts became known as Cowling's Conceit.[8]

Before obtaining the Take Note for the Summer Lodge area, Cowling had leased an area south of the Crown boundary with Wensleydale on Beezy Moor. Alexander Fothergill, agent for William Weddell, had granted him a six month Take Note for ground east of that leased to the Parkes on Oxnop Moor in January 1774. If successful, he was to have an 800 yards square area for 11 years at 1/7th Duty.[9]

After working his shafts for two years, Cowling applied to the Crown agents for a 21 year lease of this area. The Crown agents for some unknown reason declined to grant one, denying that this area was inside Crown property. This was despite having granted him the Take Note in the first place and accepting the 1/5th duty from him from 1775 to 1777. Joseph Cowling's aspirations to become a successful mine owner came to nought, hence the somewhat cynical title for his shaft at Rowntree Hole.

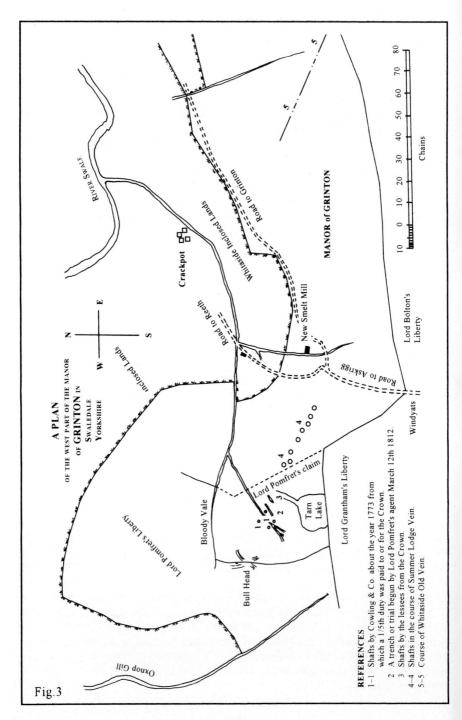

A PLAN
OF THE WEST PART OF THE MANOR
OF **GRINTON** IN
SWALEDALE YORKSHIRE

REFERENCES

1–1 Shafts by Cowling & Co. about the year 1773 from
    which a 1/5th duty was paid to or for the Crown.
2 A trench or trial begun by Lord Pomfret's agent March 12th 1812.
3 Shafts by the lessees from the Crown.
4–4 Shafts in the course of Summer Lodge Vein.
5–5 Course of Whitaside Old Vein.

Fig.3

MANOR of GRINTON

RIVER SWALE

Crackpot

Whitaside Inclosed Lands

Road to Grinton

Road to Reeth

Inclosed Lands

New Smelt Mill

Road to Askrigg

Lord Bolton's
Liberty

Windyats

Lord Grantham's Liberty

Tarn
Lake

Lord Pomfret's claim

Bloody Vale

Bull Head

Lord Pomfret's Liberty

Oxnop Gill

Chains

36

One of Cowling's partners, Hickes, went to work as an agent for Pomfret after Cowling's scheme had failed and he persuaded Pomfret to lay claim to the ground. The Crown lessees then decided to assert their boundary and oppose Pomfret by ordering their agents to cut off the water supply sending water from Summer Lodge Tarn to the Spout Gill mines and mill. The disputed ground then lay unworked for several years and a chance of getting overall control of this promising area, which would have revived the flagging Grinton Mines, was to elude Knighton and Readshaw.[10]

THE NEW ADVENTURERS

The structure of the Adventurers who subleased the various mines began to change in the 1770s from groups of working miners to the newly-emerging class of wealthy yeoman farmers, local businessmen and professional classes from the surrounding towns. These middle-class entrepreneurs were the forerunners of families who would come to dominate mining enterprise in the area for the next century. They came into the industry when the top beds were largely worked out and deeper shafts and drainage levels, requiring more capital outlay, became necessary. The financial resources required were beyond the reach of the Adventurer/Miners and this group now became dependent on the new investors for employment rather than generating their own income.

This can be seen from the list of investors in the new company set up to work Whitaside Mine in February 1775. These were Ralph Parke of Low Row, hosier and lessee of the Beldi Hill mines; Leonard Hartley, co-lessee at Beldi Hill who also worked the Middleton Tyas copper mines and was the agent for two of the Crown lessees, William Knighton and the representatives of the late Richard Turner, and took two shares on their behalf; Thomas Simpson of Reeth and Thomas Stoddart of Fremington, both mining agents at the Arkengarthdale mines; Thomas Elliott of Fremington, who had been agent for the Bathurst family in Arkengarthdale; John Langhorne and Christopher Raine of Reeth; Edmund Lonsdale, woolstapler of Richmond; Adam Bird, mining agent; Edward Elliott of Rochdale; and William Brown of Heaning.[11]

A formal agreement was drawn up in 1786 to reform the Whitaside Company. This agreement authorised three of the investors, Christopher Raine, Ralph Parke and John Langhorne, to act as a committee to direct trials, manage affairs and settle the accounts. George Emmerson of Reeth was appointed surface agent at a salary of £12 12s 0d p.a. and Anthony Harker of Reeth became the underground agent at £35 per annum. Profits were paid out twice yearly.

The Crown lessees also continued making trials at other mines in the field. For example, between 1792 and 1797, William Knighton paid out £73 3s 7d as his one-third share of the losses incurred in trials at Grovebeck, Harkerside and the New Virgin Set at Whitaside.

Despite all this activity and exploration work, production across the field declined sharply, from an average of 110 tons per annum between 1776-83 to 31 tons annually from 1784 to 1789. Production then peaked twice (see production figures on page 128) and then rose considerably towards the termination of the lease when all reserves were probably being ripped out in case the lease was not renewed.

Caleb Readshaw, the grandson of the Caleb who had purchased the manor of Grinton from Lydia Marriott, assumed the surname of Morley in 1783 when he inherited Beamsley Hall near Skipton from his uncle, John Morley. Bankruptcy proceedings against him began in the Court of Chancery in 1779 when it became clear that he was heavily in debt and mortgaged to the hilt. By a decree of the Court, his property was ordered to be put up for auction in June 1788, but the bids were judged to be too low.[12]

The case dragged on for another two years until, in 1791, James Fenton of Loversall near Doncaster made a successful bid of £8050 for the Grinton estate. The Fenton family were known as the "*Yorkshire Coal Kings*" because of their extensive ownership of collieries in the Leeds/Wakefield area. Fenton does not appear to have become involved in the mining activities at Grinton, however, despite the family's involvement with the Chacewater mines in Cornwall and copper smelting works in South Wales. The estate was purchased purely for the shooting rights and he built Grinton Lodge sometime before 1814 for use as a hunting-lodge.[13] In 1818 the estate was transferred by Deed of Gift to his son, William Carr Fenton, who subsequently sold it to Godfrey Wentworth of Woolley near Wakefield in April 1839.[14] As with the Fentons there is no evidence to show that Wentworth became involved in the Grinton Mines.

THE NEW INHERITORS

A warrant was issued for a new lease of the Grinton Mines in February 1801 to John Moore Knighton of Grenosen, Devon. The term was for 31 years at 1/8th duty.[15] John Moore Knighton was the son of William Knighton, who had died some time before 1796, and in March 1803 he assigned a quarter share in the lease to Josias Readshaw Morley of Beamsley Hall, the son and heir of Caleb Readshaw Morley, who had died in 1797. Knighton assigned another quarter to his wife and the other quarter was divided between his three daughters.[16]

Because of all the different departments the warrant had to pass through, this lease had still not been completed by May 1803. Sampson George, the lessees' agent, and John Hutchinson, the Crown Agent, were in disagreement over the amount of Duty Lead payable during this delay. Knighton insisted that the reduced Duty be payable from the issue of the warrant in 1801. In September the Lords of the Treasury instructed Hutchinson to accept the duty at the reduced rate. Further bad feeling was caused when Knighton questioned whether duty lead should have tax paid on it by the lessee or by the Crown. The Treasury Lords decided that Crown duty lead was exempt from tax.[17]

An application for a reduction of the duty lead was sent to the Treasury in November 1809 by Mrs Mary Knighton, widow of John Moore Knighton who had died in 1806/7, and Josias Readshaw Morley. Thomas Butson of Thwaite, who had been agent for the Crown lessees prior to the lease of 1803, gave evidence to support the petition. In this he cited several examples of how costs had doubled during the six years since the lease was first granted. Labour costs had risen from 1s 6d to 3s 0d per day, ash timber from 1s 3d to 2s 6d per foot, ropes from 7s 0d to 14s 0d per stone and carriage from the smelt mill to Stockton from £1 7s 8d to £2 3s 6d per 20 pigs.[18]

THE SECOND DISPUTE AT SUMMER LODGE

Thomas Butson, Mrs Knighton's agent, had been the agent for the Swaledale mines of the Pomfret Family when the Spout Gill Veins were first discovered. At that time he had prevented colliers getting coal at Windgate Colliery on Askrigg Moor, saying that all Summer Lodge as far as Haverdale Beck was part of Healaugh manor and not Grinton. When he became the agent for Mrs Knighton, however, he changed his stance, claiming the ground belonged to the Crown.[19]

As was Cowling before him, he was aware that the Spout Gill Veins must extend into the Summer Lodge area. Encouraged by Butson, the ground was let to a group of Adventurers on January 1st 1808 at a duty of one-third.[20] Josias Readshaw Morley became the major shareholder in the venture. After spending a great deal of money on trials to test the ground thoroughly, the main Summer Lodge Vein was located north-east of the Tarn in the Middle Tongue area.

This find brought a flurry of letters from John Davies, agent for the Swaledale mines, to Peter Denys, who managed the Pomfret estates. Denys replied ordering Davies to ascertain the boundary from Peter Hammond who owned the surface rights of the Summer Lodge area, but not the mineral rights.[21] Hammond then posted notice that he intended riding the boundaries of Summer Lodge in order to establish their actual extent.[22]

After this, Davies contacted a Mr Robinson who had drawn up the lease for Knighton which did not describe the actual boundaries but merely named the manor.[23] Peter Denys sent a memo to Davies to try and get a partnership to work the disputed ground, the lessees to maintain possession of it at their own expense. He was to examine the Land Registry at Northallerton and to try and find out when the late Lord Pomfret had ridden the boundaries of this part of Healaugh.[24]

Despite the initial panic by Denys and Davies, they did nothing till March 1812. Acting on Davies's orders, Joseph Cottingham & Co. dug a trial trench between Rowntree Hole and the shafts on the main Summer Lodge Vein. Butson then wrote to the Treasury Lords, giving background details of the dispute. Since July 1810, 68 tons of ore had been raised which, at an average price of £24 per ton, was worth upwards of £1650. There was also ore on the bank which, when smelted, would produce about another 300 tons. The duty payable would amount to about 37 tons. Butson noted that it would be very discouraging for the lessees, who had spent a great deal of money on trials to locate the vein, if they should now lose possession, especially as the rest of the field was producing very little ore.

The Summer Lodge Company had, by 1812, built the Summer Lodge smelt mill to deal with the large quantities of ore being raised and also constructed over two miles of road, all at a cost of between £700 and £800. They were paying a very high duty of 1/3rd and the difference between this and the 1/8th paid to the Crown was profit received by the Crown lessees.[25]

Davies sent two of his men, Thomas Whitfield and Thomas Blades, to start work again in the area and, in May 1813, written discharges were delivered to them on behalf of the Crown lessees by their agents, E.A. Knowles and John Spensley.[26] Davies wrote notifying Denys about the discharge and said that they were ignoring it. They were getting ore, which cost about £11 per fodder to work, and asked if he should let foddertale bargains. Air trunks would, however, be required as the men could not work half the time for lack of air in the workings.[27]

In the first half of 1813, 1184 pigs of lead, worth £2035 8s 1d, had been sent from Summer Lodge Mill to Stockton and, by the end of the year, the Crown lessees were only five yards from Pomfret's boundary line. Davies wrote asking what to do should they cross over into Oxnop ground.[28] Despite the legal uncertainty as to who actually owned it, the local miners were very keen to get in on the rich ground. Davies noted in one letter that two partnerships were "hot for it".[29]

In July 1814 a take note was issued by Davies to John Rider Wood, Ottiwell Wood and George Dinsdale for the area adjoining Summer Lodge as far west as Oxnop Gill. A curious situation developed in August when Ottiwell Wood transferred his third share to Josias Readshaw Morley, one of the Crown lessees working at Summer Lodge who now had a foot in both camps.[30] By September John Rider Wood & Co were making trials on the range of the Summer Lodge Vein and had paid Davies £100 up front and the first £25 half year rent. Wood asked for a full lease of the ground and offered to pay a duty of 1/5th. Davies recommended Pomfret to grant the lease "as they have proposed so as to keep possession of it at their risk and charge".[31]

Josias Morley received a letter from his agent, E.A. Knowles, in January 1815 in which he said that no legal measures had as yet been taken by Pomfret. It was Knowles' belief that Pomfret would never bring the dispute to court and would probably wish for a compromise by way of arbitration in order to gain some part of the ground, as there was no way he would obtain it before a jury.[32] In October Davies wrote that the Summer Lodge Co. were raising ore at £3 10s 0d per fodder as the ground was so soft.[33]

In October Davies examined papers from the Marriott v Wharton dispute, in which the boundary was described by various witnesses as running from Windgate Hurrack to Summer Lodge Tarn, then to Bull Head, but none of the depositions mentioned the Middle Tongue area which was crucial to Pomfret's claim. Other witnesses had declared that it ran northward from Bull Head to Bloody Wall, the word northward being the important point as this would put the boundary through the Middle Tongue ground.[34] When the papers of the Crown Agent William

Chaytor were examined in December, however, it was found that he had written Middle Tongue northwards onto the description of the boundary.[35] Early in December, Peter Denys asked Davies to contact William Chaytor and find out on whose authority he had inserted Middle Tongue northwards onto the boundary *"as without that I fear we have little or no chance"*.[36]

Understandably, Davies was getting frustrated by Denys's lack of direction, for he wrote at Christmas 1814: *"if you should get that ground you should lose no time, otherwise the lead will be carried away, you sometimes raise my spirits to get that ground and at others you let me down with a clash"*.[37]

By February 1816, Davies's actions were beginning to alarm Denys, who wrote saying that he should not *"tamper with Mr Morley to induce him to betray the interests of the Crown and the other lessees for our own interest. This would not only be disgraceful, but if it appeared at the trial would cause us to lose. Be very cautious not to talk to Morley"*.[38] The final letter came in March from Richards to Davies and stated: *"It is proposed to offer a lease to Chaytor and he then repays legal costs over the 21 years in return for his and Morley's support and to give us all the friendly assistance they can. This method is proposed as the only one that can be adopted as all the others are against the law"*.[39]

After this, interest in Summer Lodge boundaries seems to have waned, Pomfret probably realising that his claim was very weak. It is, however, more likely that ore production declined sharply after the initial bonanza. This was often the case in the Grinton field where most profit went to the first discoverers and subsequent Adventurers tried in vain to emulate their good fortune.

REFERENCES

1   PRO. Chancery Depositions. C12/1310/18.

2   YML. Hailstone MSS. Box 5. File 41.

3   PRO. CRES 2/1390.

4   PRO. CRES 2/1390.

5   PRO. LRRO. 3/85.

6   PRO. CRES 2/1390.   Hornshaw, T.R. *Copper Mining at Middleton Tyas* (Northallerton: NYCRO, Publication 6, 1975. p.112. NYCRO. Publication 37. *Alexander Fothergill and the Richmond to Lancaster Turnpike Road.* Hartley, M.; Ingilby. J.; Hall. D.S.; Wenham. L.P. 1985. p.101.

7   DRO. D/HH/6/2/248. PRO. CRES 2/1390.

8   PRO. CRES 2. LRRO 1390.

9   NYCRO Publication 37. p.101.

10   PRO. CRES 2. LRRO 1390.

11   NYCRO. ZKU.

12   Barker MSS. Charlesworth v Broderick.

13   Goodchild, J.   *The Coal Kings of Yorkshire* (Wakefield: Wakefield Historical Publications, 1978), pp.77-81.

14   Holliday MSS.

15   PRO CRES 2. LRRO 1390. NYCRO. ZQH.

16   DRO. D/HH/6/4/3.

17   NYCRO. ZQH.

18   PRO. CRES 2. LRRO 1390.

19   Clarkson MSS.

20   PRO. CRES 2. LRRO 1390.

21 NYCRO. ZLB 6/3/43.

22 NYCRO. ZLB 6/3/44.

23 NYCRO. ZLB 6/3/45.

24 NYCRO. ZLB 6/3/46.

25 PRO. CRES 2. LRRO 1390.

26 NYCRO. ZLB 3/4/26.

27 NYCRO. ZLB 6/14/4.

28 NYCRO. ZLB 6/14/8.

29 NYCRO. ZLB 6/14/11.

30 NYCRO. ZHP 0174/12 Mic 1324.

31 NYCRO. ZLB 11/14/12.

32 NYCRO. ZHP 0177/13.

33 NYCRO. ZLB 6/14/16.

34 NYCRO. ZLB 6/5/67.

35 NYCRO. ZLB 11/14/17.

36 NYCRO. ZLB 6/5/69.

37 NYCRO. ZLB 11/14/18.

38 NYCRO. ZLB 6/6/12.

39 NYCRO. ZLB 6/6/13.

THE MORLEY FAMILY (1817-1854)

JOSIAS READSHAW MORLEY

By 1817 the Grinton lessees were Mrs Mary Knighton with one quarter, Josias Morley also with one quarter and Messrs Drake, Garden and Chadwick, the husbands of Mrs Knighton's daughters, with the other two quarter shares. These lessees presented a petition early in the year to the Commissioners of His Majesty's Woods, Forests and Land Revenues, asking for a reversionary lease at a reduced duty. To support their claim, they stated that all the veins had been worked out in the Bearing Beds, apart from those at Summer Lodge, therefore the costs had increased owing to the need for deeper trials.[1]

Thomas Dickinson of Spensley Croft, Alston, was appointed to carry out a survey and present a report on the mines. His first report, sent in July 1817, stated that the only two mines which were producing ore were Whitaside and Summer Lodge and no trials were being made anywhere else on the field. The present lease stated that at least four pickmen should be engaged in trials on all the veins and this was not being complied with. He recommended that the present lease should be surrendered, on condition that a new lease be granted at a reduced duty of 1/10th. This new lease should specify veins which were to be worked.[2]

His second report, sent in November, was very critical of Morley's co-lessees.[3] He stated that *"Mrs Knighton and the rest of the family have not spent any money in Grinton during their present lease, or made any new trials in any part of the field at their own expense"*. Josias Morley, the only lessee to be involved with the mines, was a partner with the Knightons' sub-lessees at Summer Lodge. Output was declining, however, and they were having difficulties paying the duty of one-third. This duty forced them to work only the best part of the veins, consequently leaving a great part unworked owing to lack of finance for trial work. Dickinson recommended reserving Harker Vein, Birks, Brownagill, Harker End, Grove Beck and Grinton How, which the lessees claimed were worked out and abandoned, to the extent of 100 yards on either side of them. Also, special covenants should be inserted to ensure that four men were constantly employed on trials.

The Commissioners replied that, in order to encourage the new lessees, they were willing to grant the reduction in duty to 1/10th. The duty of 1/8th was to be retained, however, on the veins recommended by Dickinson. This practically covered the whole field, so they were obviously not convinced by the argument of the petitioners, who had claimed the mines were exhausted. A special clause was inserted which stated that all new veins were to be worked in a proper manner by at least four men. On default of this condition for a period of three months, the vein and 100 yards on either side would revert to the Crown.[4]

With the granting of the extended lease, new grants were made to sub-lessees as follows: Summer Lodge to Messrs Raisbeck, Metcalfe & Co. at 1/6th duty; Whitaside to Robert Raw & Co. at 1/5th; Browna Gill to Thomas Hunter & Co. at 1/5th; and Grinton Moor to Messrs Robinson, Whitelock, Morley & Co. at 1/6th.

The Grinton Moor Company was also working the Ellerton Moor Mines, under somewhat dubious circumstances as it would appear later. They discovered some highly productive ground at Ellerton and in 1820 began rebuilding the Grinton smelt mill (see below) and driving the Devis Hole Level in order to drain the Ellerton and Grinton mines.

Josias Morley, one of the partners, died in February 1827 and it emerged that he was practically insolvent. He was in debt to the miners and local tradesmen, despite having sold lead to the value of £16,000. He had also borrowed 1600 pigs of lead, worth about £2500, from his partners. Morley's executors appointed one of his friends, the land agent Captain John Harland of Marrick, to clear these debts.[5] Harland set about running the Ellerton Mines in a more efficient manner and soon succeeded in liquidating the debts of around £26,000.

Three months after the death of Josias Morley, Miss Jane Francis Erle Drax of Charborough, who owned the Ellerton estate, married John Samuel Wanley Sawbridge. After making inquiries, the latter discovered there was no actual lease of the Ellerton Mines to Morley and the Whitelocks and began what were set to become lengthy legal proceedings to eject them from the mines. By the time he succeeded in obtaining an injunction from the Court of Chancery, however, the mines were completely exhausted.

FRANCIS MORLEY
Negotiations began in 1828 for a renewal of the 1802 lease which was due to expire on December 3rd 1833. In the petition to the Commissioners, it was claimed that, as the mines were extremely poor and the price of lead very low at only £18 per fodder, it was hoped that a reduced duty of 1/10th, instead of 1/8th, might be considered across the whole field. There were over 200 men employed in the field and seven horse levels had been driven. A great many trials had been made and the lessees' profits for the past 12 years had not exceeded £300 a year. The bargains let by the Partners were at 1/5th duty. The Partners' shares were 1/4th to Francis Morley, 1/4th to Mrs Mary Knighton, and the remainder divided between Mr Drake, Mr Garden, Mrs Chadwick and Miss Wildman.[6]

Matters were delayed, however, by national events.[7] A letter sent in January 1829 from E.A. Knowles to Ottiwell Tomlin, who acted as local representatives for the partners, said: "*Mr Garden says delay sending the Memorial as the Government is in that state that scarcely any business of that description will be attended to*". Things were improving by the end of the year when Francis Morley sent a letter to Ottiwell Tomlin from London, saying: "*About 10 days ago Lord Lowther moved in the House that he should bring in a Bill respecting the granting of Crown Lands*".[8]

The Commissioners ordered John Bower, the Surveyor of Crown Lands in Yorkshire, to prepare a report on the mines, which he visited along with William Tarn, a mining agent. Bower's report did not paint a rosy picture of fortunes at Grinton, although he noted that "*in expectation that it should prove rich there has been*

erected on the waste [by the Grinton Moor Company] *a new smelting mill''*.
Summer Lodge was not producing as much ore as the previous company, while
Whitaside was only producing enough ore to cover expenses. Browna Gill Mine
employed three pickmen and here also the ore produced was only sufficient to
cover working costs. The Crown lessees themselves had expended very little of
their own money on trials and had only taken shares in Grinton Moor and Browna
Gill Mines. Their profits were derived from returns from the sub-lessees' duty
after paying the Crown duty.[9]

Bower ended his report with the recommendation that a minimum rent be inserted
in the new lease and that the field be split into separate mines.[10] The Partners
objected to this and requested that the clause which stated that they must obtain
the consent of the tenants of the enclosed lands to work in their fields and that the
latter should be compensated for damage done to their lands by any mining
activities be deleted from the new lease. On Bower's advice, this was refused.
One important proposal by the Partners, however, was that the Summer Lodge and
Cogden mines be named and inserted in the new lease. The lease to Francis
Morley and Messrs Garden, Drake and Chadwick was renewed on December 3rd
1833 to run for 21 years and 33 days at a duty of 1/7th, instead of the 1/10th
initially requested.[11]

Of the partners who obtained the 1833 lease, only Francis Morley appears to have
become actively involved as a partner in the new companies sub-leasing the
various parts of the field. The other lessees were content to receive whatever share
of the profits was forthcoming and paid very little interest in the day to day running
of the mines.

John Harland, who acted as agent for Francis Morley's mines at Hurst as well as
Grinton, received a letter from the Treasury enquiring why no duty lead had been
received by them for the period 1845 to 1846. He informed them that the duty lead
had been sent to John Wilkinson of Stockton, who had since been declared a
bankrupt. The lessees had sent 2309 pieces and the duty had been 385 pieces,
worth about £493 after charges. In view of the loss incurred by the lessees, they
were allowed to pay £246, or roughly half the Crown's duty, and a claim was laid
before Wilkinson's administrators, who paid out 2s 3d in the pound.[12]

By 1849, the 1833 partnership was crumbling. George Drake had died and his
estate was being administered by a Mr Bridgeman.[13] Mrs Chadwick had been
declared insolvent and her share was no longer valid. Another shareholder, Mr
R.J. Garden, wrote on behalf of himself and Mr Bridgeman to Langhorne &
Tomlin, solicitors for the Grinton Company, offering their shares for sale.[14] The
average proceeds of a quarter share had not exceeded £25 for the past seven
years.[15] The reply was sent offering £100 each, a sad reflection on the decline of
the mines. The offer was refused, as was another for £150. Mr Bridgeman
travelled up to the mines from Tavistock, but, instead of meeting Langhorne as
arranged, inspected the mines himself, then returned to Devon, after visiting the
Lake District and Alderley Edge mines.[16]

Mr Garden's agent, E.A. Knowles, wrote in November 1850 that the Whitaside Mines were raising good ore in the Undersets now that the Smithy Level had reached ground unworked by the 'Old Man'. Grinton Moor was very poor, however, and the New Vein near Swinston Brow was cut off, so prospects looked bad in this part of the field. The balance due to each share was £39 16s 11d. Knowles also warned in his letter that there would be local opposition when application was made for a new lease.[17]

In September 1851 Messrs Garden and Chadwick and the representatives of Col. Drake accepted an offer of £150 for their shares in the Grinton Mines. They were purchased by a local consortium consisting of Isaac Fisher, banker; Thomas Smurthwaite, banker's clerk; J.R. Tomlin, solicitor; and J.B. Simpson, solicitor, all from Richmond, and Ralph Milner of Reeth, on the understanding that the Whitaside and Grinton Moor Companies could work their ground till the present lease expired in 1855.[18]

Francis Morley began negotiations for a new lease of the mines in 1853 when he presented a Memorial to the Commissioner of Her Majesty's Woods, Forests and Land Revenues. In this he stated that it had been the habit of John Moore Knighton and his heirs to sub-let their share of the mines, which resulted in their being worked in a "*desultery fashion*" to his detriment. The duty on renewal in 1833 had been raised from 1/8th to 1/7th, but since that time the price of lead had fallen and the price of labour had risen as a result of emigration to the U.S.A. and Australia. He wished to start new levels in order to drain and explore at a greater depth, but was unwilling to commence operations till a new lease was assured.[19]

As part of the 1851 sale agreement, the old partners also presented their petition for a renewal of the lease. It had been necessary for several horse levels to be driven and railed to reach unworked ground. Owing to the length of time taken to drive in hard rock with no ore found to finance the exploratory work, the partners had failed to make a profit and had incurred a net loss of nearly £4000 since the lease was granted in 1833.[20]

To examine Morley's petition, Charles Alexander Gore, Commissioner for H.M. Woods, Forests and Land Revenues, ordered John Higgins, the Crown Surveyor, to compile a report on the Grinton mines. Higgins requested that Stephen Eddy of Grassington, the Duke of Devonshire's Mineral Agent, should be appointed to assist him, as Eddy had been very helpful to him in settling a dispute with Earl de Gray concerning the Crown Mines on Askrigg Moor. Basing the report on the boundaries set out in the newly completed Ordnance Survey map of the area, Eddy made a thorough inspection of the workings, before submitting his findings in September 1853.[21]

STEPHEN EDDY'S REPORT
At Grinton Moor the Devis Hole Level had been driven to about 180 yards from the Ellerton Boundary. The ground above the level was completely worked out by the 'Old Man', but some ore was being won from a flot below the level. In the

eastern reaches of the Grinton How and Grovebeck mines, some ore was being won, but they had both been worked at a loss for some years. At Whitaside, where the level was upwards of a mile in length, there were between 30 and 40 men at work, barely making it pay. The ground above the level, and in many parts up to 40 yards below, was exhausted by the 'Old Man'. At Summer Lodge operations had been suspended for several years. In the past numerous trials at a shallow depth had been very productive, but no regular vein had been found.[22]

Eddy concluded his report by saying that the operations of the present lessees had not yielded a considerable profit and he accepted that they had incurred a loss of around £4000, however, as claimed. There was a great deal of unexplored ground in the lower beds and, in order to encourage them to undertake deeper trials, he recommended a reduction to 1/8th.

When appraised of Eddy's findings, Harland replied to Charles Gore that he accepted the report, but proposed one small alteration. Instead of paying the duty in pig lead, he requested the option of paying in ore.[23] To justify this as being beneficial to both parties, he pointed out the newly-discovered Hugh Pattison method of making white paint from lead ore rather than from smelted lead as had been done previously. Parties compelled to smelt their ore by the terms of their lease would, therefore, be deprived of an advantage enjoyed by the Teesdale and Weardale lessees who paid duty in ore.[24]

Higgins asked Eddy's opinion on this matter and the latter pointed out the failings in the reasoning behind Harland's request. The effect of the concession would be to throw the cost of smelting on the Crown, and the fact that the lessees held the mills meant that they would be able to exact unreasonable terms for smelting such ores. To avoid this situation, Eddy recommended duty payment be taken in money or ore at the option of the Crown. This was agreed to by both parties and a clause was inserted in the new lease which was due to start on the 5th January 1855. The term was 21 years at 1/8th duty and the usual one pound annual rent, and no fewer than 25 pickmen were to be employed.

THE CONSORTIUM (1854-1875)
The new partnership which obtained the lease with Francis Morley was made up of James Brown Simpson, solicitor; Isaac Fisher, banker; Thomas Smurthwaite, banker's clerk; James Robinson Tomlin, solicitor, all from Richmond, plus Ralph Milner of Reeth, miller, and John Harland of Marrick, land agent. These men were part of a powerful group which held a virtual monopoly on all the Swaledale and Arkengarthdale lead mines, as well as on the coal mines in the Tan Hill area. They possessed considerable knowledge of mining gained from this close involvement and it is likely that this was the first time in their history that the mines would be worked in an effective manner. Unfortunately, it was now too late as the 'Old Man' had just about exhausted the field and no more large discoveries would occur.[25]

THE HARLAND - MORLEY AFFAIR

Francis Morley, one of the partners, died in August 1854 soon after the lease was granted and his estate was found to be massively in debt. John Harland, another partner at Grinton, was also agent for Morley's mines at Hurst and, by careful management, had helped to rescue the family from debts left after the death of Morley's father, Josias. Unfortunately for Harland, the family repaid this good work by accusing him of cheating them of £16,000 which Josias Morley had left to his children in his will.[26] Two legal actions began in the Court of Chancery. John Bailey Langhorne, on behalf of Morley's creditors, brought a suit against Harland and Morley's widow, Charlotte, and in turn Morley's widow brought an action against Harland.[27]

In the action Charlotte Morley v Harland, heard in 1856, it was decreed that an account should be drawn up of all monies received by Harland since 1848 when, out of loyalty to the family, he had agreed to become assignee of Francis Morley's debts. This showed that £13,112 had been repaid, leaving the sum of £3000 outstanding. Harland refused to pay this money and the Court ordered the sequestration of his shares in the Grinton, Whitaside and Summer Lodge mines. Further orders were granted by the Court against Harland in 1862 and 1863, but again he refused to comply. The final outcome of this rather unsavoury affair is not known, but it ended the involvement of the Morley family in the mines which had begun with Caleb Readshaw 100 years before.

John Harland was so upset about his treatment by the Morleys that he published an account of the affair for public distribution. At the beginning of the paper he quoted from Hamlet: "*Virtue itself 'scapes not calumnious strokes*". In 1873 the English Dialect Society published "*A Glossary of words used in Swaledale*" also written by Harland, which included the famous Swaledale poem he had written, Reeth Bartle Fair.[28]

To repay Morley's creditors, the court ordered that his shares in the mines be put up for sale at public auction. This was held at the Buck Inn at Reeth on February 6th 1857. Morley's one-quarter share in Whitaside was sold to Ralph Milner for £110, while the one-quarter share in Summer Lodge, which the sale bill stated had not yet been worked, went for £72 to William Lister, who also paid £850 for the one-third share in Grinton Moor mines.[29]

THE DECLINING YEARS

The new partnership set up to work Whitaside in 1855 consisted of John Barker, Thomas Smurthwaite, John Richard McCollah, James Robinson Tomlin, Ralph Milner, Edmund Coates and the representatives of Isaac Fisher with a 1/8th share each, while Francis Garth of Crackpot and the representatives of George Alderson of Arkengarthdale held the other 1/8th between them. Ralph Milner was appointed as the managing partner, with Adam Barker as agent. Each partner had to deposit £50 with the Swaledale & Wensleydale Bank towards capital for working the mines. The old duty had been 1/7th in pig lead, plus five per cent, but this had now been lowered to 1/8th, plus four per cent, with the option to sell in either ore or pig lead. Previously the lessees had been bound to smelt at Grinton Mill, but this no longer applied. The duty was paid four times a year and was paid in money, rather than lead, at the same price as the company sold its stock.[30]

In 1858 the Commissioners of Land Revenue ordered that annual reports on the Grinton mines should be made. Warrington Smyth, one of the founders of the Geological Survey, was appointed to carry out the inspections.

In his first report, submitted in November 1858, Smyth observed that, considering the extent of the field, which was about five miles in length and a mile wide, the amount of operations were in his own words *"trifling"* judged by the standards of other mining districts. One of the chief obstacles to proper development was that shares were concentrated in the hands of a few local people who, although genuinely interested in legitimately working the mines, lacked sufficient capital to develop them. The lessees therefore, although wishing to employ as many people as possible, tended to place most of their men on exploratory work which could be subsidised by ore-getting in other parts of the field, hence the local expression *"that a given mine cannot bear more than so many dead men"*. This was borne out on the day of his visit when 10 men were dismissed at Grinton Moor after the water had risen in the workings and stopped ore-getting. The introduction of public companies would be beneficial in inviting a bolder system of mining, but the high level of Royalties in the Dales was too restrictive to invite the outlay of large sums of money for speculative results.[31]

On his visit the following year, Smyth found the situation little changed, with ore from Devis Mine subsidising development work at Whitaside. He found considerable quantities of zinc (silicious calamine) at Grinton and Whitaside, which had been neglected both by the miners and lessees, who all appeared totally ignorant of its presence. Samples sent by him for assay had yielded above five per cent of metallic zinc. As no zinc was being worked in Yorkshire then, Smyth was unsure as to the best course of action to be taken in the Crown's interest.[32]

By 1860 the lessees were becoming desperate and in May of that year they sent a memorial to the Commissioners, asking for a reduction of the duty to 1/12th. The reason cited was that they did not realise when they took the lease that the field had been so thoroughly worked out in the upper beds. In order to reach deeper reserves, they would need to drive at least two new horse levels. One at the east end of the ground would take at least seven years to drive at an approximate cost of £5000. To open up the Summer Lodge ground at the west end of the field would require two new adits at a cost between £1000 and £1200.[33]

When Smyth visited Grinton in February 1861, he found that work had already begun on a new level at Whitaside which had been driven nearly 300 fathoms at a cost of £1500 on a vein which was so far barren. At Devis the miners had broken into what he described as *"a remarkable labyrinth of natural passages"*. Through these, he was able to make his way nearly quarter of a mile beyond the Crown boundary into Ellerton ground. He proposed that a new level be started in Cogden

Plate 1. Cogden Gill Deep Level, begun 1861 (R.F. White, 1995).

Gill from which a branch could be made under the How Mines to drain both the Devis and the How Mines. He also suggested lowering the duty to 1/12th, but necessary new work should be strictly defined. This should include the deep level from Cogden, exploratory work at How and Grovebeck, and either a shaft or a level at Harkerside. The new level at Whitaside should be driven with no fewer than four men at least 300 fathoms south of the present forehead, and a new level should be started at Summer Lodge.[34] The request for the duty to be reduced from 1/8th to 1/12th was granted by Charles Gore in November of that year.[35]

The lessees were obviously encouraged by the reduction and, when Smyth visited Grinton in December 1861, he found that work had already started on the Cogden Gill Deep Level. The first site chosen had to be abandoned after a few fathoms because of bad ground and a fresh start was made lower down. At Harkerside, a level had been started near the mouth of one of the old hushes and was in about 15 fathoms. At Whitaside, the new level had collapsed near some old workings which proved that, even at this depth, the 'Old Man' had *"ransacked the ground"* to a greater depth than had first been realised. At Whernpot Shaft, west of Whitaside, work was going well with two crosscuts put out east and west at a depth of 10 fathoms. The Summer Lodge Level was being driven by four men, but they would need to drive 100 fathoms before reaching ore.[36]

THE KINNAIRD COMMISSION

The Grinton Mines were visited in 1862 by Charles Twite, who was employed to examine the Richmond mining district for the Kinnaird Commission which had been set up to enquire into working conditions in mines. His first inspection was made at the forehead of the main drive east on Wellington Vein in Devis Hole Level, where he took samples of air for analysis. At this time, the crosscut was 200 fathoms from the adit mouth and was being driven in the shale on top of the Main Lime by one man and two boys. It was six feet high and five feet wide and ventilation was natural, via an old air shaft about 175 fathoms inbye.[37]

The Commissioners themselves visited Reeth in March 1863 and interviewed several local mine agents, doctors and investors. Adam Barker, aged 55, agent for Whitaside and Summer Lodge mines, was one of the first to be interviewed. He had begun driving Summer Lodge Level the previous October and four men were employed in driving the forehead. At Whitaside an average of 15 men had been employed for the past six years in Smithy Level, which was 550 fathoms in length and ventilated by two rises to day. Barker had adopted the following ingenious method of providing extra ventilation in the level. An old door had been cut down to fit the size of the level and attached to the front of the first wagon. This pushed air into the mine when going in and pushed foul air out when leaving. He had named this device after Dr George Robinson of Richmond, one of the partners in the Whitaside and Summer Lodge Companies. The Commission also interviewed Ralph Milner, one of the shareholders at Whitaside and Summer Lodge.[38]

THE FINAL PUSH

After visiting the mines in 1864, Smyth attended a meeting at Richmond where the various partners proposed the division of the field into two or three separate parts. This would make it possible for the lessees to abandon those parts which were evidently unworkable and concentrate their resources on the mines which were paying. Smyth was very favourable to this view and thought it would benefit both the partners and the Crown. The work could be concentrated on the best mines which would not have to prop up the poorer mines, leaving more finance to invest in the more profitable and promising ventures. This view, however, fell on deaf ears at the offices of the Land Revenue Commissioners.[39]

The Whitaside Company had its hopes raised in 1865 when a Mr Backhouse became a shareholder. In the belief that he possessed the backing of his family's banking business, several new trials were started, but, when called upon to bear his share of the costs, it was discovered that he was the black sheep of the family and possessed no means to pay his call. The trials, however, did bring some hope when a 16 fathoms sump into the Underset Chert in the Old Whitaside Level found a string bearing reasonable ore. Using a hand windlass to raise the ore, this working supported the efforts on the rest of the field for the next two years.[40]

On Smyth's recommendation, the Summer Lodge Company installed a grinding mill in 1867. The vein was about two feet wide and had been worked for about 160 fathoms from the head of the crosscut, but the ore was poor in quality.

51

By 1869 the mines were going into decline. The Cogden Deep Level, driven by Robinson & Co., had still not drained the ground it was intended to on Grinton Moor and the How. A new company, the Grinton & Ellerton Mining Company, was formed in order to extend the drives on Wellington Vein into Ellerton ground. The Whitaside company was heavily in debt to the Swaledale & Wensleydale Bank and, on top of having to pay a duty of four per cent to the main lessees, it was almost financially crippled.[41]

REFERENCES

1 NYCRO. ZHP. Mic 1324.

2 PRO. CRES 2. LRRO 1390.

3 PRO. CRES 2. LRRO 1390.

4 NYCRO. ZHP. Mic 1324.

5 Harland v Morley. Private publication.

6 DRO. D/HH/6/4/13.

7 DRO. D/HH/6/4/14.

8 DRO. D/HH/6/4/19.

9 PRO. CRES 2. LRRO 1390.

10 PRO. CRES 2. LRRO 1390.

11 PRO. CRES 2/211.

12 PRO. CRES 2/1390.

13 DRO. D/HH/6/4/24a.

14 DRO. D/HH/6/4/24.

15 DRO. D/HH/6/4/23.

16 DRO. D/HH/6/4/24a.

17 DRO. D/HH/6/4/31.

18 DRO. D/HH/6/4/105.

19 DRO. D/HH/6/4/4. PRO. CRES 34/212. File 1441/1.

20 PRO. CRES 34/212.

21 PRO. CRES 39/61. For a biographical note on Eddy, see Gill, M.C. *Yorkshire and Lancashire Lead Mines: A study of lead mining in the South Craven and Rossendale Districts* (Sheffield: NMRS, British Mining No.33, 1987).

22 PRO. CRES 34/212.

23 Hugh Pattison's Improvement in the Manufacture of White Lead by means of Carbonate of Lime and the Chloride or Nitrate of Lead, Patent Numbers:-

8627	10th September 1840
9102	24th September 1841
12,479	14th February 1849
13,519	18th February 1851

24 PRO. CRES 34/212.

25 DRO. D/HH/6/4/6.

26 Harland. J. Harland v Morley. Private pub'n.

27 DRO. D/HH/6/4/7.

28 Harland. J. *A Glossary of words used in Swaledale, Yorkshire* (English Dialect Soc., 1873).

29 DRO. D/HH/6/4/7. Sale particular in Tyson MSS.

30 DRO. D/HH/6/4/28.

31 PRO. CRES 34/213. LRRO. 1441/2.

32 PRO. CRES 34/213. LRRO. 1441/2.

33 PRO. CRES 34/213.

34 PRO. CRES 34/213.

35 DRO. D/HH/6/4/6.

36 PRO. CRES 34/213.

37 British Parliamentary Papers. (Kinnaird) Commission on Mining Accidents, Vol.7 (Reprinted: Irish University Press, 1969), p.322.

38 Kinnaird Commission. pp.399-401, 403-404.

39 PRO. CRES 34/213.

40 PRO. CRES 34/213.

41 PRO. CRES 34/213. File 1441/2/4591.

THE CHARLESWORTH FAMILY (1855-1946)

Joseph Charlesworth Dodgson Charlesworth of Chapelthorpe Hall, Wakefield, purchased the Manor of Grinton in June 1855 when the previous owners, the Wentworth family, were forced by mounting debts to sell off parts of their property. The Charlesworth family, like the Fentons before them, were members of the newly-rich Victorian colliery masters with pits at Barnsley, Leeds, Rotherham and Wakefield.[1] It is a strange quirk of fate, but owning this estate seems to have been a harbinger of bad fortune. The business interests of James Fenton, who had purchased the Grinton estate in 1791, began to decline soon afterwards and it was the same with the Wentworths in 1855. History would repeat itself early in the next century when the Charlesworth family business began to fall apart, mainly because of the actions of the grandson of J.C.D. Charlesworth. With Charlesworth's purchase in 1855, the wheel turned full circle as all the owners were from the same area of South Yorkshire.

Described as a forceful character, Charlesworth was a J.P., Freemason, and Deputy Lieutenant for Yorkshire, but gained a certain notoriety for his activities in the political field. He was elected M.P. for Wakefield in 1857, but, after two years in office, was defeated by the candidate who had stepped down at the previous election. Corrupt practices were alleged and the Parliamentary Inquiry resulting from these disenfranchised the Borough for some years. It was found that Charlesworth had spent some £3500 over and above the amount declared to

Plate 2. Grinton Lodge, used as a shooting lodge by the Charlesworth family, now a Youth Hostel (L.O. Tyson, 1994).

the election auditor, his opponent having spent £100 less, and allegations were made of intimidation and bribery. During the election, the finances had been handled by his cousin, John Barff Charlesworth, a barrister, who was imprisoned for two years for the offence before receiving a Royal Pardon.[2]

As with many of his contemporaries, Charlesworth purchased the Grinton estate, which contained 390 acres of moorland, principally for the grouse shooting, but he soon caught the lead mining bug and became involved with investment in other lead mines in the area.[3] The Charlesworths used Grinton Lodge (now the Youth Hostel) mainly as a shooting lodge till 1946 and attended Grinton Church and supported local activities. The interest in lead mining was further expanded when his cousins, Joseph and William Charlesworth, became involved with the lead works at Llanerch-y-mor near Flint in the late 1880s after their marriages to the daughters of Adam Eyton.[4]

SALE OF THE MINES
The Crown Lease was due for renewal in January 1876 and J.R. Tomlin wrote to the Commissioners in November 1875 asking if they would agree to divide the field up into three parts. One part would be leased directly from the Crown by himself, another section by G.A. Robinson and the third section by J.C. Birkbeck.[5] At the beginning of December, a letter was sent to Charles Gore at the Land Revenue Office by Messrs Brown, Wilkinson & Scott, solicitors, enquiring if the Crown's mineral rights were for sale. On behalf of J.C.D. Charlesworth, they were instructed to offer £4000 for the mineral rights.[6] Charles Gore replied on December 29th that he had considered the division of the field, but, as most of the ore in the field appeared to be exhausted, he would recommend acceptance of the sale, providing a new lease be granted to the previous lessees on the same terms.

The lessees delayed their decision on renewing the lease, so, after several letters from Charlesworth's solicitors, the £4000 was paid to the Land Revenue Office in April 1876. The Crown Warrant was granted on May 16th 1876, with the proviso that a new lease be granted to the old lessees and backdated to January 5th if requested. The old lessees were Thomas Smurthwaite of London, James Robinson Tomlin of Richmond, Ralph Milner of Reeth and George Alderson Robinson, gentleman, the surviving descendants of the partners in the lease of 1857.

Despite several requests, Charlesworth's solicitors had not seen a copy of the draft conveyance in January the following year. The reason given for the delay by the Crown Solicitor was that he had been waiting for a disclaimer to be signed by Tomlin, Milner, Robinson and the Swaledale & Wensleydale Bank as assignees for Smurthwaite and this had not been received till April 3rd 1877. In a report made on April 5th, the Crown Solicitor stated that the Crown lessees had declined a new lease and had sold their mining equipment, including the How Mill, to Charlesworth. His solicitors then requested the clause for the new lease be omitted from the conveyance. The Deed of Conveyance for the mineral rights was finally enrolled on May 1st 1877, bringing to an end nearly 800 years of Crown ownership of the Grinton mines.[6]

After J.C.D. Charlesworth's death in March 1880, the Grinton estate passed to his son, Colonel Albany Hawke Charlesworth, J.P. M.P. An enthusiastic Christian Scientist, he visited America in 1912 to see Mrs Mary Baker Eddy (the movement's founder) having sold Chapelthorpe in 1900 and moved to Manchester.[7]

THE SWALEDALE MINING ASSOCIATION

An indication that a renewal of mining activities was to begin at Grinton came with an article in the *Craven Herald* dated September 3rd 1887. This noted that the Whitaside mines had been inspected by a group of mining engineers, including William Henry Hosking of Newton Abbott, John Retallick, manager of the Hurst Mines, and John Ascough Rodwell, manager of Keld Heads Mine. They were accompanied by John Barker, Colonel Charlesworth's agent, and Dr McClure, surgeon, of Woodford, Essex.[8] A further article appeared on September 24th saying that Colonel Charlesworth's duty was to be 1/17th, which was considered very low, and he had promised that the first £25 from the mine's duty would go towards building the proposed Conservative Club Room at Low Row.[9]

The air of optimism was ill-founded, however, for the men behind this venture were London-based share speculators. Hosking and McClure, along with another speculator Faithful Cookson, were involved with the Hurst mines from 1881 to 1889. These, like Grinton, if worked honestly, may have become a successful mining venture. Hosking and Cookson, however, had also been involved with hyping an iron mining enterprise in 1866 at Eskdale in Cumbria and owned several iron mines in Cornwall and Devon.[10] Even if the motives behind the developments at Grinton were genuine and the expected ore was found in the Underset Lime, the use of Haggs Gill Level instead of the Low Level would mean that workings would have to be under the adit and expensive to work.

On October 4th 1887, the Swaledale Mining Association Ltd was incorporated, with Dr Thomas McClure as one of the directors and J.A. Rodwell as agent. The company secretary was James Kendrick Lamb and the registered office was 16 Great Winchester Street, London. Lamb was also the secretary of the Yorkshire Lead Mines Company, which worked the Hurst Mines.[11]

By November, eight men had been put to work in the Smithy Level at Whitaside. In the following year, William Henry Hosking, acting for the Swaledale Mining Association, was granted take notes by A.H. Charlesworth on 13th February to search for lead ore in the remaining areas of Grinton for 18 months. By this agreement, the company was allowed free use of the smelt mill and any equipment left at any of the dressing floors.

THE GRINTON MINING & SMELTING COMPANY LIMITED

Hosking made a positive report to the Association and, in order to raise more capital, a new company, the Grinton Mining and Smelting Company Ltd, was incorporated on the 25th April 1888. This company had the same secretary and registered office as the Swaledale Mining Association and McClure as one of the directors. A nominal capital of £50,000 in £1 shares was proposed. By an agreement signed on August 24th, it was decided that, in exchange for the mining rights of Hosking and the Swaledale Mining Association, the Grinton Mining and Smelting Co. Ltd would grant 10,000 of its shares to the Mining Association and 20,000 to Hosking. This was a tactic used by Hosking and Cookson with other companies they formed. Colonel Charlesworth, who had granted an unusually long lease of 42 years with the duty on a sliding scale, and his wife were the largest shareholders in the new company holding 700 shares between them.[12]

John Rodwell, the mining agent for Grinton, was also agent for the Keld Heads Mine on the other side of the watershed in Wensleydale. He put into action a plan to drain a large water-logged area in the Ten Fathoms Grit, known as the "*Swelly*", from the Grinton side. This would have made trials possible in the lower limestones, which had been rich at Keld Heads.

The mine which was intended to be the mainstay of the operation at Grinton was Devis Hole Level and, in order to reach the known large ore reserves lying in flots below water in the soles of Devis, it was necessary to first drain the swelly. Once this scheme succeeded, it would unwater 22 fathoms of virgin ground which was known to be rich in lead ore. This was to be accomplished by extending the deep crosscut from Haggs Gill Level, which lies 105 feet lower than Devis, and by a drive on Robinson Vein in Devis towards Haggs, connecting the two drives with a sump.[13] Further details of the work done at Devis Hole are given in the sections covering the Grinton Mines and the Ellerton Mines.

At Whitaside the main intention was to work a barytes vein from Smithy Level. An old shaft had been reopened and they had discovered a solid rib of carbonate of barytes, 12 inches thick and of excellent quality, which Rodwell estimated would cost £1 per ton to raise and sell at £3 5s 0d per ton. Work also started in opening up Musgrave's Level at Grovebeck.

An article appeared in the September 16th edition of the *Craven Herald* in 1892 painting a glowing picture of the state of the mines. The Deep Drainage Level had drained part of the deep grits, it reported, and this had resulted in a rich new vein being recently found. The correspondents had met a miner coming down from the mines who told them that he had that day got a solid piece of ore weighing about two hundredweight. The new lode was taking a southerly direction, possibly bringing it under the Wensleydale side of the boundary, presumably at Cranehow.[14]

Sadly, this optimistic report failed to convey the true state of affairs. Rodwell's regular reports to the *Mining Journal* end in October 1891, often a harbinger of bad fortune. What the events were which led to the end of mining at Grinton is not known at present and to surmise at this point would be unjust to Rodwell who obviously had very high hopes for the success of the venture. A total of 99 tons were smelted between 1890 and 1892 from Grinton and three tons from Whitaside. The Mineral Statistics show the mine as standing in 1894. The Grinton Mining & Smelting Company was officially dissolved on December 31st 1895.[15]

The Charlesworth family was decimated in the Second World War. Major Albany Kennett Charlesworth, who succeeded his father in 1914, died in an aircrash on the way to the Yalta Conference, and his only son, David, died in a motorcycle accident in Palestine. The Grinton Estate was sold by Major Charlesworth's executors to Major W. Parlour of Middleton St George, and R.J. Colling, a racehorse owner.[16] At the time of writing, the mineral and shooting rights and the freehold were owned by Mr L.B. Holliday of Mount St John, near Thirsk.

REFERENCES

1   Goodchild. J. *The Coal Kings of York-shire* (Wakefield: Wakefield Historical Publications, 1978). p.144. Speight. H. *Romantic Richmondshire* (London: 1897) p.223.

2   Goodchild. pp.141/2.

3   PRO (Kew) BT31/3151/1273.

4   Goodchild. p.135.

5   PRO. CRES 34/214.

6   PRO. CRES 34/214.

7   Burke, J.B. *Dictionary of Landed Gentry* (London: Harrison, 1898), p.389. Goodchild. p.150.

8   NMRS Records - *Craven Herald*. September 3rd 1887, page 6, column 4.

9   NMRS Records - *Craven Herald*. September 24th 1887, page 5, column 3.

10   Tyson. L.O.*A History of the Manor and Lead Mines of Marrick, Yorkshire* (Sheffield: British Mining No.38, 1898), p.57. Austin. A. ''The Mines of Eskdale'' *British Mining*, No.43 (1991), p.135. M.C. Gill pers comm. Mrs B.M. Howard pers comm. Mrs Howard, a member of NMRS, is studying the activities of Cookson & Hosking and would welcome any information on them.

11   PRO (Kew) BT31/3957/25100.

12   NMRS Records - *Craven Herald*. November 12th 1887, page 2, column 6. PRO (Kew) BT31/26497/4119.

13   Rodwell, J.A. Prospectus for Grinton Mining & Smelting Co. Ltd, August 31st 1888. Barker Mss. *Mining Journal*. September 15th 1888, p.1042.

14   NMRS Records - *Craven Herald*. September 16th 1892, page 3, column 6.

15   Burt, R. Waite, P., Atkinson, M. & Burnley, R. *The Yorkshire Mineral Statistics 1845-1913* (Exeter: Department of Economic History, University of Exeter, 1982). p.31. PRO (Kew) BT31/26497/4119.

16   The late Elsie Pedley, pers comm.; Edward Pedley, pers comm.; Lawrence Barker pers comm. Goodchild, p.144.

THE GRINTON MINES

DEVIS HOLE MINE

Robinson, Whitelock & Co. began this level in the 1820s. The cost of driving was greatly reduced when it cut and followed a series of caverns near the top of the Main Limestone. By 1858, drifts on Wellington Vein were near the boundary with Ellerton in the east and Devis Hole Gill in the west, whilst Cranehow and Robinson's Veins, with their associated flots, had each been worked south-east for over 400 yards. Unfortunately, much of the ore was found under the level and had to be worked from sumps, which was expensive. During the 1860s, therefore, a much deeper level was driven towards the mine from Cogden Gill. This was the Low Level, but it never reached the veins and was abandoned around 1870. Despite being said to be near exhaustion in 1865, Devis Hole limped on, with some small discoveries of ore, until it too was abandoned in 1875.

When the Grinton Mining & Smelting Company Ltd took the mine, it decided that Haggs Gill Level, in Ellerton, was the key to the Devis ground. Work on clearing out this level, which was blocked by two falls, had started by September 1888. Six men were also working around the clock in Devis Level to clear and widen the previous company's drift towards Haggs on Robinson's Vein. Drawing in Devis had been let to two men and a boy at 15 shillings per fathom, and, when not employed in drawing, they were to assist in clearing the drive beyond the sumps on Robinson Vein.

Haggs Level was cleared as far as Redway Head Vein by October 1888, and the men were pushing through broken ground towards the Grinton boundary, only 147 fathoms away. There were then only 106 fathoms to drive before the connection would be made. In Devis, the drift on Robinson's Vein heading towards Haggs was clear, with all the sumps in repair ready to raise ore as soon as the water was drained. Driving in the Deep Crosscut was slowed down in January, however, as the forehead had reached a bed of hard grit. This resulted in the men driving only three and a half fathoms that month. A permanent airway, providing fresh air for the men and allowing some water to be drained, was made by the end of the month.

There remained only seven fathoms to drive to make the connection in the Deep Crosscut by February and the durkways near the swelly in Robinson's Vein were being repaired. Twenty-five fathoms had been timbered, with 40 fathoms more requiring timber before the deep sump on the swelly was reached. By March, a further six fathoms had been driven and they had cut a strong lead with a two foot throw, running at an angle of 35 degrees to Robinson's Vein, which was letting in water freely. The men had now taken the driving on bargain at £3 per fathom, paying the cost of candles, explosives, tools etc. themselves.

Clearing the Deep Durkways to make the connection with Cranehow Bottom Vein near the swelly was also being pushed at all speed. The principal durkways from the far south sump in Cranehow were only 18 fathoms away from the swelly. These durkways in Robinson's Vein had been driven south towards Cranehow from

Devis by the previous company and it was down a sump in these durkways that, in the 1860s, Hird and his 15 partners had raised eight tons of ore in a single day. They had been drowned out the following day, however, since when it had never been worked. In the next sump along, the late manager, Robert Wharton, had said there were large reserves at a depth of only four fathoms. In another sump, called Allen's Sump, the men told Rodwell they had raised several tons of ore and had been forced to leave large blocks of solid ore which were too heavy to raise, before the water drowned them out. The miners were already putting in bids to take these sumps on bargain as soon as the water was drained, giving some indication of the richness of the soles.

The Deep Crosscut drive on the lead from Robinson's Vein in Haggs was directly under the line of the top level on Robinson's Vein in Devis by March. Work was going well as they were driving in plate and shale, containing a great quantity of douk (decomposed limestone or earthy vein filling, which could include clay minerals) with traces of blende and spar, although water was seeping in from the sides. Driving had been let to six men at £2 per fathom. In May, a trial rise was started to prove their position in the beds and to determine if it would be possible to drain the swelly at this point. After 11 fathoms, they were into the grit with a strong feeder of water coming in and this promised well for draining the swelly.

With the draining of the swelly now becoming imminent, Rodwell began work clearing the two bottom drifts on Cranehow Bottom Vein, which had been suspended owing to waterlogged ground caused by the swelly. The old workings here had reached as far north as the Ellerton boundary at Lunton Hill, where natural caverns had been found on the same horizon as those in Devis Hole. The Deep Drainage Crosscut would, when completed, also succeed in draining the sumps in this mine and, when a connection was made to Devis, utilising the natural caverns to make driving easier, it would form a connection with Devis. The two drifts, one 45 fathoms and the other 49 fathoms, needed clearing out and widening to take waggons, and four men were set to work at five shillings per fathom for one and 7s 6d per fathom for the other. They were also to clear the old sumps and lay rails. By January 1889, the men were into ore-bearing ground to the north west of the old drifts which had been untouched by the Old Man. The drive continued in what became a solid string of ore till, by March, they had cut Close's Flot, the main objective of the crosscut. When a 14 feet deep sump was put down into the flot, however, they were stopped by water. Work was then halted till the swelly could be drained, but the ground was so promising that a bargain had been let on the back ground at 35 shillings per bing.

GRINTON HOW MINE
The Redmire road from Grinton winds steeply up for about 1½ miles before levelling out onto a short plateau which approximately marks the top of the Main Limestone. How Hill is the north western corner of this plateau, overlooking the dale. Immediately before the road begins to rise once more, How Vein crosses it from north east to south west. On the east of the road are Blenk's and Ridley's Hushes and the Low Ventilator shaft, while to the west the vein runs up toward

DEVIS MINE

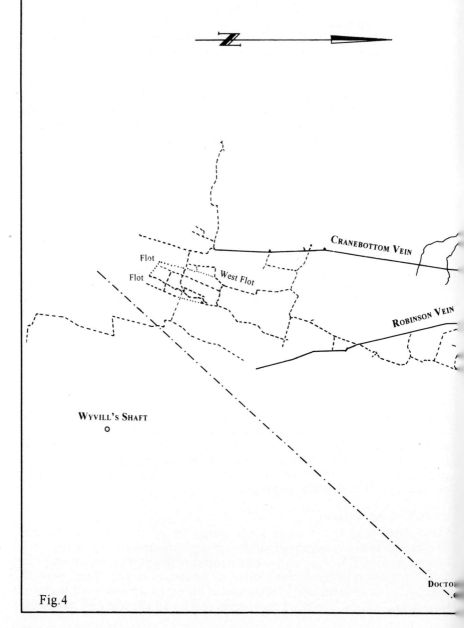

CRANEBOTTOM VEIN

Flot

Flot   West Flot

ROBINSON VEIN

WYVILL'S SHAFT

DOCTO

Fig.4

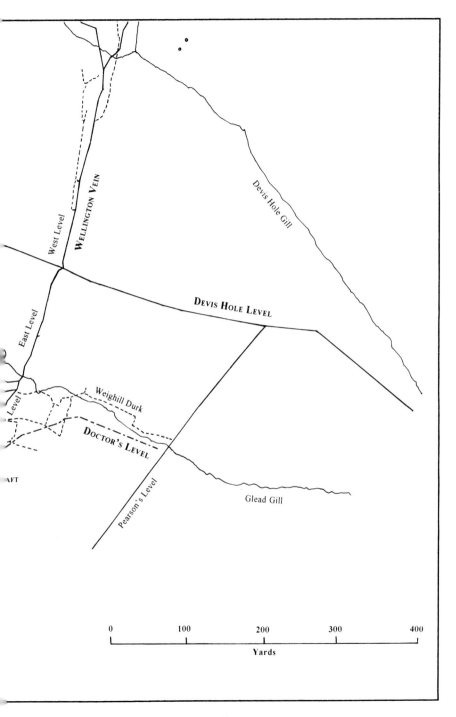

Devis Hole Gill

WELLINGTON VEIN

West Level

DEVIS HOLE LEVEL

East Level

Level

Weighill Durk

DOCTOR'S LEVEL

Pearson's Level

Glead Gill

AFT

| 0 | 100 | 200 | 300 | 400 |

Yards

Bolton Greets. Back towards How Hill, a north branch of How Vein is marked by a line of shafts crossing the plateau. Of these, High and Low Swang Shafts are the most obvious. Between these branches, replacement ground was worked in the beds of the Richmond Chert. Mineralisation of the veins themselves was probably patchy though occasionally rich, as at the Low and High Ventilators which were producing most of the ore in the manor during the period 1758/9.

Grinton How Mine was one of the earliest workings in the manor, and it is likely that the North Vein was the first to be discovered close to How Hill, hence the name of the mine. The mine was worked by Humphrey Wharton and Lord Scrope in the 17th century, but the value of £6 given in the 1650 Survey suggests it was of little value then.[1] Lord Wharton's Shaft is one of the highest up How Rake, close to the final rise towards Bolton Greets. Mining was concentrated in this area until the middle of the 18th century and throughout this period occasional rich strikes, such as that by John Ozell, excited disputes culminating in Swale v Marriott and Wharton v Marriott and Marriott's final victory, discussed above.

The most productive period in the history of the mine was that of Reginald Marriott and his son, another Reginald, between 1696 and 1736. They sublet the working of the mine, probably by the bargain system, and also undertook the driving of a drainage level, allowing a greater depth of working.[2] However, all this work was still restricted to the high part of the vein above the plateau just below Bolton Greets (see fig.2).

The 1750s saw a short revival of the mine's fortunes with the discovery of the extension of the south branch of How Vein. This was in the Main Limestone to the east of the road. Blenk's Hush worked the outcrop, and the High and Low Ventilator Shafts were sunk to work the vein in depth. Ridley made trials in the Main Limestone on Sharrow Hill on the opposite side of Cogden Gill to look for an extension of the vein, but the trials were too far to the south and the vein appears to become unproductive before crossing the beck.

Thomas Rosewarne's Bargain Book shows how the mines were let. Four yearly bargains were made in 1758 to several groups of miners at a duty of 1/5th, plus 15 shillings per fodder. On Grinton How, the North Rake was let to John Emmerson. He had one meer west of Hallam Shaft and five to the east. On the Sun Rake, 4½ meers at the Low Ventilator were let to Thomas Dun and partners, followed by seven other bargains along the vein, ending with that of Tobias Cradock who had a length between the Whim Shaft and Lord Wharton's Shaft. The account of ore raised in 1758/9 shows that for the last three bargains, totalling about nine meers and all let to members of the Cradock family, the ore was raised at the Whim Shaft. The bottom four bargains, totalling 15½ meers and controlled by Thomas Simpson, were worked from the High and Low Ventilators. The centre bargain, of one meer east of the Low Cow Shaft and three to the west, was let to John Alderson.[3]

In 1762 the ground was again let on 4½ year bargains. Thomas Dun and Robert Elliott were to work six meers of ground at the Low Ventilator, and Christopher

Raine and partners were to work four meers of ground at the end of John Alderson's Low Cow Shaft ground. The North Vein had been included in James Simpson's bargain of Grovebeck.[4]

How Level was driven from the foot of Blenk's and Ridley's Hushes, starting in the middle part of the Main Limestone and then running into the underlying shale. The level allowed some ore to be won from the old shafts, but, although the vein was driven upon for at least one mile, it proved disappointing. Cooper's Level (using the same tip as How Level) was driven north into the North Vein, also with little success. North east of these levels, Swinstone Brow Level was driven to work the Underset Limestone, but, after showing initial encouragement, in 1850 the vein was found to split into small strings with very little ore.[5]

Like the other levels on Grinton manor, How Level was probably started in the 1820s. Mention is made in 1850 of How Level forehead in an old dial book of Captain Harland's, but it is not clear whether it was still being driven then.[6] The next positive period of work was from 1859 to 1867. In 1859 five men were driving an exploratory drift (Swaledale cross cut?) and in 1861, when production at Devis Mine dropped dramatically, 27 men were set on to find new deposits in How Level. The 'Old Man' was found to have worked all the ground before them, but work continued until 1867 with a dwindling workforce and some ore was raised, chiefly from old workings.[7]

REFERENCES

1   PRO. CRES 34/213 File 1441 (2)   5   DRO D/HH/6/4/31

2   DRO D/HH/6/4/2 Petition of Wm Knighton   6   Leeds Central Library: Backhouse MSS

3   NYRO ZKU 1X 1/43 Bargain Book   7   PRO. CRES 34/213 File 1441 (2)

4   Ibid

GRINTON HOW MINE

Surface   Works   as   in 1774

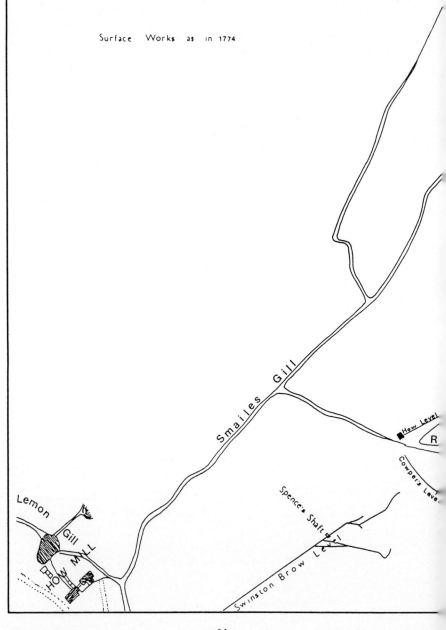

Smailes Gill

How Level

R

Cowper's Level

Lemon

Gill

MYN L

HOW

Spence's Shaft

Swinston Brow Level

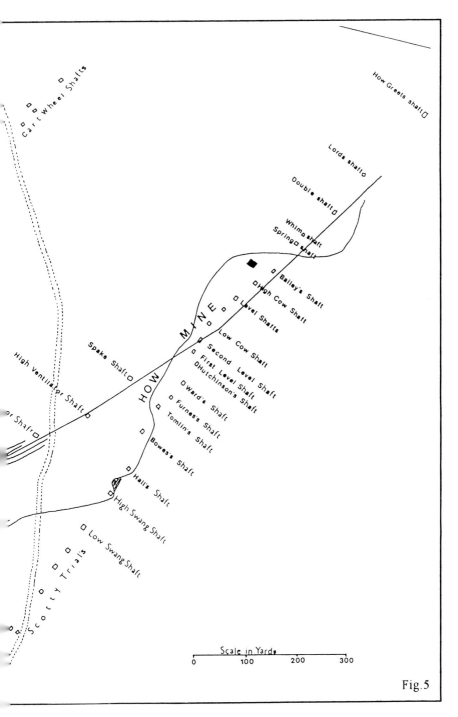

How Greets shaft

Lords shaft

Double shaft

Cart Wheel Shafts

Whims shaft
Springs shaft

Bailey's Shaft

High Cow Shaft

Level Shafts

Low Cow Shaft

Second Level Shaft

First Level Shaft

Hutchinson's Shaft

Ward's Shaft

Furness's Shaft

Tomlin's Shaft

Bowes's Shaft

Hall's Shaft

High Swang Shaft

Low Swang Shaft

Spake Shaft

High Ventilator Shaft

or Shaft

HOW   MINE

Scotty Trials

Scale in Yards

0   100   200   300

Fig.5

65

GROVEBECK MINE

This mine, at the head of Grovebeck Gill, worked a vein running more or less parallel with How Vein in the direction of Gibbon Hill from a point close to the fence crossing the mine track. The Main Limestone forms an outcrop above the track leading from How Hill Quarry to Grovebeck Level. Several hushes and shafts tried the eastern end of the vein between the level and the fence. The most productive ground, however, was between the gill to the east of the level and the foot of Gibbon Hill.

Dating all the workings is impossible, but in the 1760s the ground was split into several areas according to the number of meers granted on the range of the vein. The two lower areas proved to be of little or no value in terms of ore production, but are of great significance in the siting of smelting mills. In the latter half of the 18th century some confusion arises as to the exact sites of the mines named eg. High and Low, New and Old Grovebeck.[1]

The earliest surviving lease is dated September 29th 1761 and is to Thomas Dunn & partners who discovered ore with their first shaft, which was sunk five fathoms directly onto the lode. This would have been a flot in the Red Beds Limestone. In the six years to November 1768, the deposit produced 3556 bings (1422.4 tons) of ore. It was still producing about five fodders per week in 1768 with about 100 hands employed above and below ground, though it was considered to be nearly worked out.[2] James Simpson had a bargain for Lower Grovebeck and in 1763 bargained for Upper Grovebeck next to the Wensleydale boundary. No trial had been made at Upper Grovebeck by 1768, but Simpson was making a trial for an underset at Lower Grovebeck with 20 hands employed and had produced 19 fodders by 1768.[3]

Work continued at Grovebeck for the rest of the 18th century, but on a much reduced scale. In the period 1774 to 1782, lead returns are given for both the Old & New partners, so it appears that the mine was split into at least two areas. Fowler Hickes & Co. leased part of the mine in 1774, but, after one year's work and £300 spent in trials, the amount of ore raised was hardly paying expenses. Production figures for 1774 to 1786 for High, Low and New Grovebeck mines show a marked reduction in output, with only New Grovebeck showing any significant returns.[4]

At least two levels were driven in the early 19th century. These were Davis's Level (a hand level) driven at the top of the Main Limestone from a shake hole south towards Smithy Shaft, and Grovebeck Horse Level at the bottom of the Main Lime. Grovebeck Level was driven in the early 19th century to work the Main Limestone and drain all the shafts from Bowes Shaft westward. However, little ore appears to have been found at this horizon. The Underset Limestone was worked from the level by a number of sumps and would appear to have been productive to some extent. A rise from Grovebeck Level was put up close to the First Whim, enabling the First, Second and High Whims to be drained and ore left by the 18th century miners to be worked. Although a considerable amount of work must have

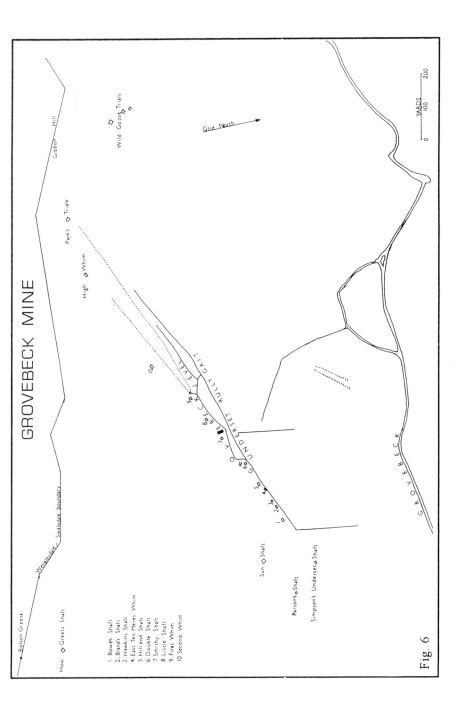

GROVEBECK MINE

Bolton Greets

How ◇ Greets Shaft

Wensleydale Swaledale boundary

Gibbon Hill

Park's Trials ◇

Wild Goose Trials ◇

High ◇ Whim

Grid North →

1. Bowes Shaft
2. Bland's Shaft
3. Hawkins Shaft
4. East Ten Meres Whim
5. Hill end Shaft
6. Double Shaft
7. Smithy Shaft
8. Little Shaft
9. First Whim
10 Second Whim

GUNDERSET GULLY GAIT

OLD LEVEL

100

90

80

70

60

50

40

30

20

10

0

Sun ◇ Shaft

Parson ◇ Shaft

Simpson's Underset ◇ Shaft

GROVEBECK

YARDS
0   100   200

Fig. 6

been done in the level, judging from the size of the tips, no reference has been found which gives a date for its driving. On the available evidence, work probably began around 1820, with a further period of working in the 1840s and 1850s. The cost of level-driving at Grovebeck appears in John Davis's papers for 1819, but this would most likely be for driving Davis's Level, which probably pre-dated Grovebeck Horse Level.[5]

In 1853 it was said that the mine was poor and had worked at a loss for some years. By 1858 the mine is noted as not working and three years later, seven men were only exploring the old workings. Four men were working in 1865 and only two in 1868.[6]

By September 1888, the Grinton Mining and Smelting Company was reopening the mine, starting with the clearance of Grovebeck Level. By January 23rd 1889, however, it was found to extend a great deal further than previously thought and Rodwell concluded that the 'Old Man' had worked Musgrave Flot. The company had cleared the level for 115 feet beyond the last of the *"old south shafts"*, with *"quite a change of beds at the far end"*. By March 1st 1889 three of the 'Old Man's' drifts in the area of Musgrave Flot had been cleared and the backed up water was being drained off. The forehead of the south drift showed indications of ore and clearing the old sumps was going well. Work continued until at least May 8th 1889, when the sumps in Grovebeck Level were being tried.[7] Rodwell also sank a shaft on the line of Grovebeck Vein, near the old Kendalls Shaft.

Judging from the language used in the *Mining Journal* reports, the Company knew nothing of the extent of the mine, which suggests that it had been closed for a long time. Complete plans of it were not available, but judging from the Company's reports, the old miners had made a very extensive search of the ground and nothing had been left to find.

REFERENCES

1 NYCRO ZKU 1X 1/43 & PRO MPPE 531

2 DRO D/HH/6/4/2

3 PRO LRRO 3/a5 XC 4276 CL

4 NYCRO ZQH 11/4 Mic 1169 & PRO LRRO 3/85 4276 CL

5 NYCRO ZLB 3/11/29

6 PRO. CRES 34/213 1441 (2)

7 *Mining Journal* 11/05/1889, p.548.

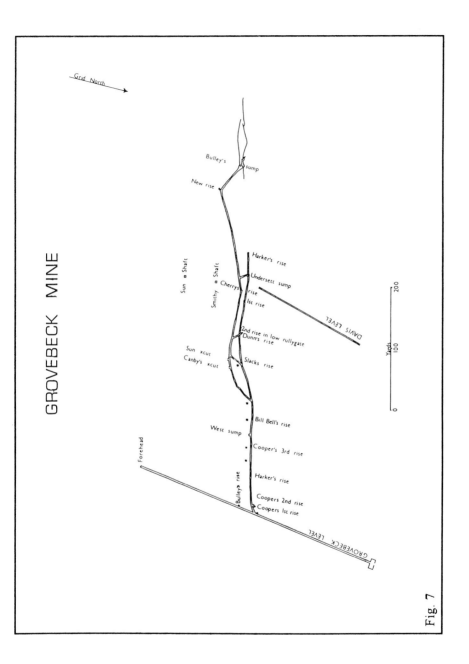

GROVEBECK MINE

Fig. 7

HARKERSIDE MINES

Half a mile west of Grovebeck Level, a hush worked the Harker Vein for a distance of half a mile over the high point of the saddle formed by High Harker Hill and down the hill on the other side. A small trial level driven in 1861 in a westerly direction, from a point just a few yards from the eastern end of the hush, prospected the ground to the south of Harker Vein. After being driven 200 yards by 1862, it had cut *"Flotty ground"*, but without finding ore, as the flots had probably been worked out by the shafts to the south of the saddle in which direction the level points.[1]

Several strings were worked to the north of the main vein, mainly by hushing, but two shafts were also sunk onto a small string on the north side of the hush nearest Grovebeck. Further along the hillside towards Brownagill, several shafts and hushes mark possible other veins and flots, some of which appear to have been very productive.

A level was driven from the foot of the hush on the dale side of the saddle in a SSE direction back towards Grovebeck. This would have been able to work the Underset Limestone, as well as the Main Limestone. This level was mentioned in 1761 when the mine was let to Robert Elliott and partners. It is likely that it was driven by Marriott earlier that century.[2]

The mine had been a prosperous one for many years and in 1650 it was valued at £20 p.a., which compares well with Whitaside at £22 per annum.[3] Around 1626, George Carter was working the mine and at the end of that century much of Sir Solomon Swale's mining was done at this mine, too.[4]

In 1766 the mine was let to John Lee who, with 10 men, raised 3.3 fodder in 1768. Such a small amount suggests that the mine had been virtually exhausted by that time. The mine continued to be worked on a dwindling scale, however, and in 1774 it was let to James Stoddart who spent £40 on trials, but only raised £20's worth of ore, again with 10 men employed.[5] For many years then the mine remained unworked and was probably abandoned from about 1800 till 1861. Mention is made in 1873 of the richness of the flots associated with Harker Vein, but it is not clear whether or not it was being worked at that time.[6]

REFERENCES

1 PRO. CRES 34/213 File 1441 (2)

2 PRO ZKU 1X 1/43

3 E317/26 pff 5045

4 E134. 9 Will 3rd T[rin] 18

5 PRO LRRO 3/85 XC4276 CL. & CRES 2/1390

6 PRO MPE 531. Dunham, K.C. & Wilson, A.A. *Geology of the Northern Pennine Orefield. Vol 2 Stainmore to Craven* (Memoirs of the Geological Survey, H.M.S.O., 1985).

BROWNAGILL AND GUY MINES

Between Harker Mine and Birks Mine were two others. They were Brownagill Mine at the head of Brownagill, and Guy Mine a little to the west. Both mines appear to have worked flots, although a Brownagill String is mentioned in 1873. The Park brothers had a share of Brownagill in the 1760s, and in 1830 Thomas Hunter was working the mine with three pickmen. Very little ore was being won then, though it was paying expenses. About 200 yards up from the ford near the shooting hut, a level was driven southwards towards the shafts above. This may date from about 1830 and is mentioned in 1840.[1] Two men were picking over the old ground in 1862 and in 1865 four pick men were at work raising a little ore.[2]

REFERENCES

1   Backhouse MSS. Captain Harland's dial book.   2   PRO. CRES 34/213 File 1441 (2)

Plate 3. Building at the portal of Smithy Level (L.O. Tyson, 1994).

71

WHITASIDE MINE

Whitaside mining ground extends from Birks West Pasture to a line from Sod Dyke Nick to Goodwell Seat, and from the Wensleydale boundary to the south to Haverdale beck and the river Swale to the north. Encompassed within this ground are several strings and veins, the most important being Birks, or Mason Rake, Mine to the east, the Whitaside/Apedale Vein and the Virgin String at the head of Ashpot Gutters, and a series of small strings on Far Greena Hill. Below the Reeth to Askrigg road the enclosed fields are also crossed by a number of strings running from south west to north east. These were tried, but proved unproductive.

The workings on Far Greena Hill, or the *"Old Field"*, are probably among the earliest in Grinton and are the most likely site of the *"halfe a more mere"* left in Christopher Conyers' will in 1504.[1] They comprise a series of shallow opencasts in the Main Limestone with adjacent dressings and bale smelting. By 1708 mining was still concentrated here and in the area around Smithy Level entrance, the southern extension of Whitaside Vein not being discovered until 1761.[2]

Birks, or Mason Rake, Vein runs across Birks West Pasture where several shafts were sunk into the 3rd Limestone finding rich ore during the latter half of the 18th century. It then continues onto the moor where Green Hill Mine worked flots in the Main Limestone. These workings also date from the 18th and early 19th centuries and Thomas Chapman & Co. were probably working this mine in 1761.[3]

Whitaside Vein enters Grinton manor close to Crackpot hamlet and runs more or less south east to the Wensleydale boundary and Apedale Head Mine. At the head of Ashpot Gutters two branches, one known as Harker's Vein, were worked. Musgrave Flot, between the branches, was rich for ore in the 1760s and became the subject of a law suit (see page 27). From the spread of shafts to the south of the vein, it is evident that there were other strings and flots associated with it, one of the most notable being the Virgin String which was tried in the 1790s.[4] The most productive part of Whitaside Vein was in the length from Smithy Level mouth to the Wensleydale boundary, a distance of about one mile.

In 1758, after the mine had been idle for about 10 years, Richard Lonsdale took a 10 fodder bargain. After raising over eight tons, mainly by hushing, he set out 10 meers of ground in 1761 with the Hush dam at the centre. This was in the Old Field at Far Green Hill. In 1759 and 1760 he hushed on the west side of Long Gill, but only raised about 12 stones of lead and so gave up to concentrate on the old mine. In April 1761 John Harker & Co. applied to work part of Whitaside and, in June 1761, leased the area around Ashpot Gutters to the east of Lonsdale's trial hush at the head of Long Gill. By December they had discovered Harker's Vein (a branch of Whitaside Vein) at a cost of £21. Harker's workings were centred on Dreadnaught Shaft. Richard Lonsdale and partners began working Whitaside Vein just a few yards to the east of Harker's workings from a shaft at a mine called Fearnaught. It was over this area that the long and bitter dispute arose. The ground leased to Harker and partners included the ground to the east of Greena Hill (Far Greena Hill), apart from that worked by Thomas Chapman & Co.[5]

The Surveyor General, R. Herbert, records that 400 people were employed around Whitaside Mine in 1768, yet in 1775 this number was down to 80.[6] On the face of it, 400 seems incredible. Where did they all live and work? Around 100 women and children, employed to dress the ore, fetch and carry etc, would be included in this number. If we assume five shafts per mine, with 20 miners to each shaft, the remaining 300 miners could have been distributed between the three mines at Whitaside. As to where they lived, many of the miners on Grinton Moor came from Wensleydale as well as Swaledale. Bolton Castle was split into tenements and several houses in the village of Castle Bolton were split into two to house the influx of miners in the late 18th century. Apedale, now unpopulated, then had at least four houses and the parish registers record several births there.

One very important point to consider is the effect that the demand on labour would have had on the mines in Wensleydale. Chauncy Townsend was the Duke of Bolton's lessee of the Apedale mines and the immediate effect would have been to force up his wage costs or deprive him of his work force. Townsend was a sharp character and no doubt jealous of profits being made on Grinton manor. He saw his chance when the Crown lease came up for renewal and made a play for the mines of Grinton, but failed.[7] In 1805 James Townsend, Chauncy's son and heir, and partners were still working the Apedale Mines, but one of the partners, Mr Smith, was accused of working on the Swaledale side of the hill to the neglect of Apedale. It is not clear whether Townsend was also involved, however, or in which area of Grinton manor Smith was working.[8]

Plate 4. Waterwheel pit for the crusher near Bradbury's and Smithy Levels at Whitaside Mine (L.O. Tyson, 1994)

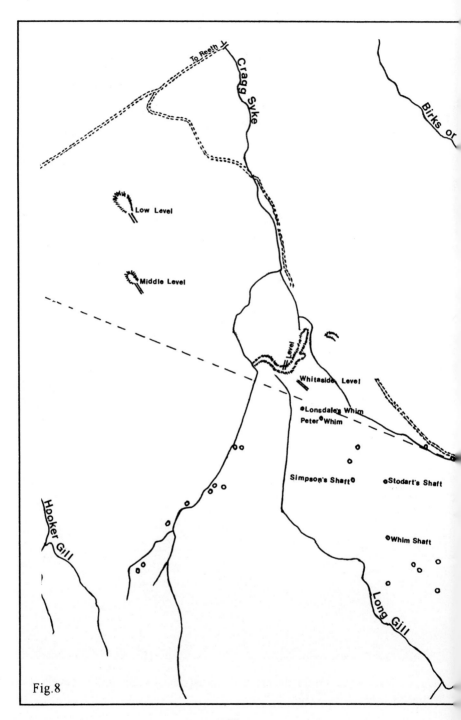

Fig.8

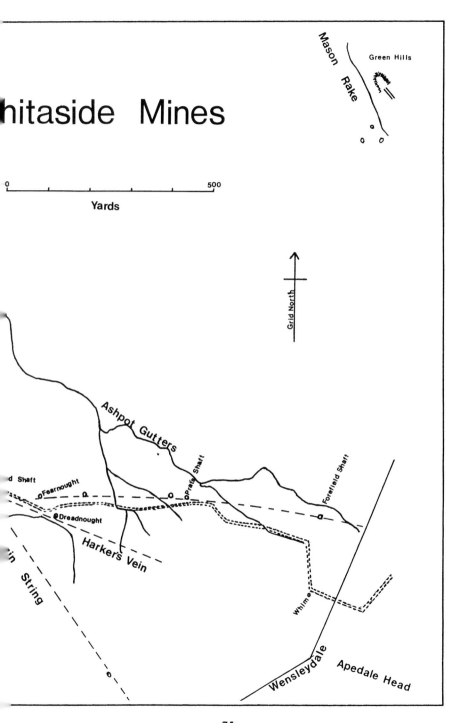

hitaside Mines

Mason Rake

Green Hills

0 500

Yards

Grid North

Ashpot Gutters

d Shaft

Fearnought

Prate Shaft

Forefield Shaft

Dreadnought

Harkers Vein

String

Whim

Wensleydale

Apedale Head

From September 1772 to March 1774 Whitaside Mine was the only mine producing ore within Grinton manor.[9] Simpson & Co. leased the mine in 1774 and spent £700 in a major series of trials which, although having only produced £300 worth of ore by 1775, led to the most prolonged period of prosperity of the mine. This lasted until 1799, when the ore began to run out. The most productive ground was still at the head of the vein in a flot approaching Apedale Mine and the Wensleydale boundary.[10] Despite a large amount of ore being raised in 1800, it was difficult to get it to market because the increased cost of oats was forcing up the price of horse transport. A year later, the mine was expected to fail because of dwindling reserves.[11] There followed a period of decline with a small amount of reworking of old ground. This occasionally produced sufficient ore to pay expenses, as in 1830 when worked by Raw & Company.

During the 1840s, the Whitaside Co. began a major redevelopment of the mine by driving *"Smithy Horse Level"* to drain the old workings in and above the Main Limestone, as well as to develop the Underset Limestone which they believed to be unworked. Indeed by November 1850 the Undersets were producing well, but by 1853, when the level had been driven upwards of a mile, it was discovered that the 'Old Man' had worked to a depth of 30 to 40 yards below the horse level.[12] At this time, the mine was yielding a small profit and keeping 30 to 40 men employed.[13] Then, once again, decline set in.

In 1858 ore getting was restricted to picking over the old works and some small strings. A new level, the Low Level, had been driven 21 fathoms deeper than Smithy Level and, after 176 fathoms, cut two veins. These were sunk upon and tried in the lime below, but found to be unproductive. This Low Level is the first one reached from the Reeth to Askrigg road. It was driven from the north side of Whitaside Vein and the two veins mentioned above were branches of Whitaside Vein. The level was driven under Smithy Level in the vein and, by February 1861, had reached 300 fathoms and cost £1500. It was discovered that the 'Old Man' had worked down to this level too, probably from Lonsdale's Whim, close to Smithy Level entrance. A rise was put up to Smithy Level and sumps sunk 20 fathoms from the Low Level, but without success. At this time the Flank Level from Smithy Level was driven, but also without success.[14]

1865 saw an improvement when a rich vein was discovered in the Underset Chert below Smithy Level, close to the junction with Harker's Vein. By 1867 this vein was producing most of the ore in the manor. By September 1868, however, it had split into strings and, because of difficulty with bad air and the cost of raising the work 16 fathoms to Smithy Level, there was little profit left.[15]

A new Low Level was begun in 1866 from the side of Haverdale beck below Crackpot village. The key-stone is initialled J.B., which probably refers to John Barker, one of the partners. This may be the nephew of the John Barker mentioned on page 46, as the latter died in 1855, The level, however, seems to have been abandoned before the mine closed in the 1870s.

In 1888 the Grinton Mining & Smelting Co. reopened the mine, first driving two hand levels whose locations are unknown. One of them, called Bradberry's, may be the level driven directly underneath the tips of Smithy Level. If this is so, then it tallies with the company's heading for Thompson's Flot, east of Smithy Level (See fig.9 - Thompson Drift). An attempt was also being made to work a barytes vein, and some of the sumps in Smithy Level were reopened and some small parcels of ore raised. The mine probably closed when reports about it cease in mid 1889.[16]

REFERENCES

1 Raistrick, A. *Mines & Miners of Swaledale* (Clapham: Dalesman, 1955).

2 PRO LRRO 3/85

3 ibid

4 Morley Account

5 PRO LRRO 3/85 & Chancery Papers

6 ibid

7 DRO D/HH/6/4/2

8 ZBO 1X 1/18/73

9 PRO. CRES 2/1390

10 NYCRO ZBO 1X 1/14/348

11 NYCRO ZQH 6849

12 DRO D/HH/6/4/31

13 PRO. CRES 39/61

14 PRO. CRES 34/213 1441 (2)

15 ibid

16 *Mining Journal* 09/03/1889, p.291.

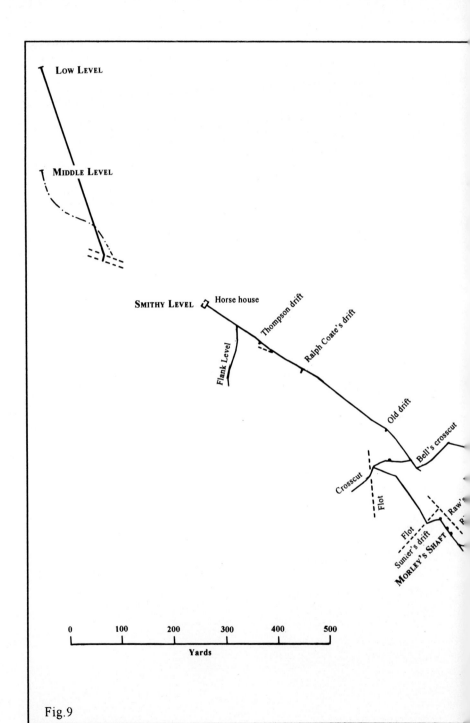

Fig.9

WHITASIDE MINE

N

ne Quarry

Parson's crosscut

Underset sump

Whittle's crosscut

Metcalfe's crosscut

Thos Bell's rise

Heslop crosscut

Dales durkway

George's crosscut

Cherry's trial

Whittle's crosscut

sump

A. RAW'S STRING

REYNOLDSON'S STRING

CHERRY'S STRING

Undersets

MURTON FLOAT

Random of Harker's Vein

VIRGIN STRING

WHIM SHAFT

SHAFT

SUMMER LODGE MINES

Summer Lodge mining ground extends westward from the Sod Dyke Nick/ Goodwell Seat boundary of Whitaside Mine to the limit of Grinton manor on the watershed of Summer Lodge and Satron Moors. The area of mining operations ended at the Reeth to Askrigg road, with only two coal levels on the east side of it, near the junction with the Summer Lodge track. Within these boundaries, there were three areas of lead mining. The most important were along the line of Summer Lodge Vein, but some shafts were also sunk onto a small SW to NE vein which crosses the road at a right angle between the smelt mill and the enclosure wall of Summer Lodge Pasture. In the beck below the mill, a level was driven, presumably to try this vein. However, it is not possible to state exactly in which direction it ran. The tip is of reasonable size and the level could have been turned southwards to test the Summer Lodge Vein in the beds below the Main Limestone. A second, parallel string cuts across the southern end of Summer Lodge Pasture where a hand level was driven south east, but without success.

The main workings on Summer Lodge Vein can be split into the East Mine, to the east of Summer Lodge Tarn, and the West Mine, to the west between the tarn and the watershed of Summer Lodge and Satron Moors. Both mines were worked from shafts sunk eight to ten fathoms into the Richmond Cherts, or the top of the Main Lime, where flots were discovered.

The East Mine starts near the junction of the track from Summer Lodge and the Askrigg to Reeth road. It worked west to above the crest of the hill, as seen from the smelt mill and the foot of the ridge called Tarn Brow. The shafts form a belt about 100 yards wide, which shows the importance of working flots as opposed to a single vein. Indeed, in 1853, it was stated that *"no regular vein had been found"*.[1] Immediately north of Summer Lodge Tarn the number of shafts diminishes and is followed by a stretch of about 250 yards with only an odd trial shaft.

The West Mine worked the main Summer Lodge Vein and Cowling Rake or Crackpot Moor Vein. The Summer Lodge Vein continues from the dead ground mentioned above across the head of Dry Gill and on over the Middle Tongue into Satron Moor where it was known as Stotter Gill Vein. On the west side of Dry Gill, Cowling's Rake joins Summer Lodge Vein from the North East.

Stotter Gill and Spout Gill mines on Satron Moor had been worked from the 17th century. Early in the 18th century they were worked successfully by the Company of Mine Adventurers of England, which must have raised interest in finding an extension to the vein on Summer Lodge Moor.

In 1774 the ground was let in two lots. One of eight meers to Joseph Cowling & Co. comprised the West Mine. The other, of 10 meers, was let to Thomas Cowling & Co. At the West Mine, two shafts (New Shaft and Cowling Conceit) were sunk in the Main Lime, close to Rowntree Pot on Cowling Rake. Ore was discovered, but work was soon suspended when Lord Pomfret claimed the mine to be part of Satron Moor (see fig.3).[2]

Summer Lodge Mine

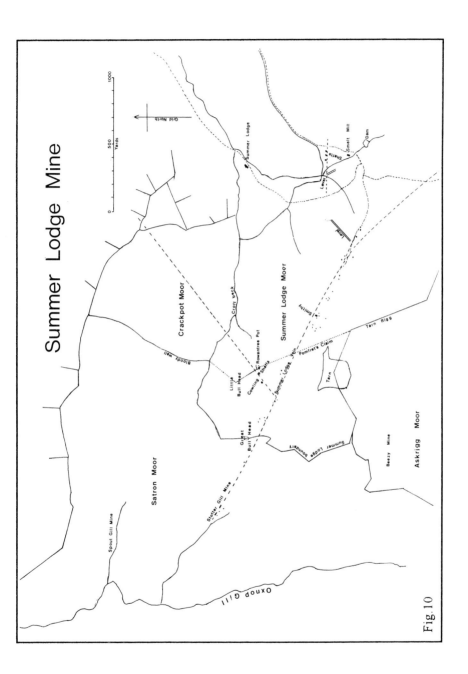

Fig.10

81

Plate 5. Bouse teams at Summer Lodge Mine. (R.F. White, 1995).

Although some ore had been raised in the 1770s, the first real success came in 1810 when the Summer Lodge Co. found good ore within the disputed ground. The dispute continued until the final settlement in 1822, with rival companies working the ground, and Thomas Butson, once an agent to the Pomfret/Denys families, changing sides when he became agent for the Crown lessees.[3]

Mining continued until the 1830s from shafts sunk 50 to 60 feet from surface to reach the flots. In the years 1810 to 1816 these paid well, but were hampered by poor ventilation and relied on natural drainage. In May 1813 it was reported, *"Raising Ore in disputed ground west of Summerlodge would pay at £11 or £12 per fother, but short of air, men can only work half of their time"*.[4] In October 1815, John Davies (Lord Pomfret's Agent) reported that the *"Summerlodge Co. is working a very rich mine in the ground in dispute Satarn Moor, they are getting lead there as loe as £3 10s 0d per fother."*[5] The productiveness of the mine is echoed in the duty paid to the Crown lessees of 1/3rd, but the unfortunate effect of such a high duty was to stifle capital expenditure. Between £700 and £800 was spent in building a new smelt mill and roads, but little or nothing on exploration or level driving.[6] The Low Level, below Summer Lodge smelt mill, is shown on Clarkson's Map of Swaledale in 1848, but nothing else is known about it. It may have been a small trial level on a vein which crosses the beck at the level entrance. The level may also be one of those mentioned below and may have been enlarged or extended in 1861.

After standing idle for a period, work started again in 1858 when one partnership of miners was raising a small amount of ore in the old shafts. Levels were proposed in 1860 and driving began in 1861, the top level cutting the vein at the end of 1862. Never very productive, the vein was followed to the west and by 1867 the workings had reached 160 fathoms along the vein. It was from 18 inches to two feet wide, but the ore was of low quality, being intermixed, and so required crushing for which purpose a crushing mill had been erected. Throughout this later period, only a small number of men were employed. There were six in 1865 and ten in 1868, when the level had been advanced only a further 40 fathoms.[7]

REFERENCES

1   PRO. CRES 39/61 Survey of Grinton Mines

2   PRO. CRES 2/1390 George Jackson's Survey of Grinton Mines April 1775.

3   PRO. CRES 39/61 Letter to Commissioners from Thomas Butson March 24th 1812.

4   NYCRO ZLB 6/14/4

5   NYCRO ZLB 6/14/16

6   PRO. CRES 2/1390

7   PRO. CRES 24/213 1441 (2)

THE ELLERTON MINES

The Ellerton mines are not part of Grinton manor, but they have been included because of the common links of investors and geology and, in later years, the common use of Haggs Gill Level.

The Ellerton mining ground is effectively split into two areas by the Great Stork Vein which runs north of, and roughly parallel with, the road from Grinton to Leyburn. It then runs eastwards across the head of Juniper Gill through into Stainton Moor. The Great Stork Vein is actually a major fault and its effect is to throw the Main Limestone down to the north where it outcrops above Cogden Hall. A series of veins, or strings, with associated flots, traverse this northern ground, the most notable being East End Vein and James Raw's Rake. In addition, Redway Head or Bells Vein, Haggs Gill Vein and Wellington Vein pass through the fault. South of the fault, the Main Lime is lifted above the level of the road and it forms an outcrop on Sharrow Hill. The beds on the south, or hanging wall, side of the fault dip in a southerly direction towards Wensleydale, forming a basin called a "*swelly*" by the miners. This prevented water draining naturally to the valley side via the Main Lime and was the main problem to be contended with in the Ellerton and Grinton mines.

The workings north of Great Stork are mainly pre 1790. James Raw was working in Grinton manor in 1760, which gives an indication for the date of his working James Raw's Rake.[1] The presence of a bale smelting site on Ellerton Moor, near the cattle grid above Cogden, suggests an early date for mining. The earliest documented mining was in connection with Simon Scrope's discovery of a lead mine in his manor of Stainton, on the eastern extension of the Great Stork Vein in the late 17th century. Simon and his son Simon continued to work their own mines and also those on Ellerton Moor under lease from the Drax family. A dispute arose in 1714 when Henry Drax discovered that the lease had lapsed and began working the mines himself, with some success. This prompted Simon Scrope to reassert his rights to the lapsed lease, without success. No details are known of Henry Drax's work, but in 1754 the mine was leased to a partnership of local businessmen and miners, while in 1755 part of the mines and the smelting mill were leased to William Sutton.[2] In 1768 one of the Park brothers paid £5 19s 0d for his share of the mine, plus £3 1s 10d in 1769, which suggest fairly modest works.[3] From at least 1683 to 1768, the ore was carried down Haggs Gill to be smelted at the Ellerton smelt mill, near the ford over the Swale on the track to Marrick.

At several points along the Great Stork Vein flots occurred. These were worked by shafts in the 18th century, then, in the early 19th century, they were drained by Derbyshire Level which was driven from the head of Juniper Gill in the Ten Fathom Grit, and further west they were drained by Haggs and East End Levels which were driven below the Main Limestone.

South of the Great Stork Vein, Redway Head and Haggs Veins run towards the Wensleydale boundary, whilst Wellington Vein runs west into Grinton Moor. The major workings were on Wellington Vein, which was also worked in Devis Mine on Grinton Moor. The age of the workings is uncertain, but the flots were worked from at least 1753 when shafts were shown on Redway Head Vein.[4] William Chaytor worked this part of Ellerton Moor (Chaytor's Shaft) in 1792 when the mine was said to be "*heavily watered*", a continual problem.[5] Wellington Vein was discovered whilst working the flots associated with it and with Redway Head Vein, c1815, probably shortly after Chaytor had given up the lease after 1811. Wellington Vein was not being worked in Grinton manor in 1817, suggesting that work then was limited to Ellerton Moor. Earlier trials had been conducted on Grinton Moor near Devis Hole (a large shake hole to the north of Wellington Vein). This was let to James Raw in 1762, but within seven years he had only raised about 1½ bings of ore.[6]

Following Chaytor's lease, Josias Readshaw Morley took a share of Ellerton mines, along with the Whitelocks of Cogden Hall. They were to be the only beneficiaries of Wellington Vein, which on Ellerton side proved profitable in the Red Beds Lime, along with Redway Head Vein, until it was exhausted c1828.[7] In June 1810 William Chaytor believed Ellerton Moor to be the richest mine in the country, yet by 1818 its small production was included with that of other small mines to give a total of 50 tons.[8] The same company worked Wellington Vein to the west in Grinton manor using whim shafts. The vein was worked from the Red Beds to the top part of the Main Limestone, where flots were also found, but, because of the high cost of lifting the work and water, the shafts were soon abandoned. Haggs Gill Level on Ellerton Moor and Devis Level on Grinton Moor were then driven to drain the shafts and, in the case of Haggs Level, to prospect the Underset Limestone.

The Grinton Moor mines were showing promise in the 1820s, when Robinson, Whitelock & Co. rebuilt the How Mill and began driving Devis Level.[9] The level was driven in the top part of the Main Limestone for much of the way in an open cavern. This reduced development costs considerably, but, owing to its position above the flots in the Main Limestone, the ore still proved expensive and difficult to get out. By 1858 the level had been driven in Wellington Vein close to the Ellerton boundary, but with little success. Robinson's Vein had been driven on for a considerable distance and flots were discovered six to eight fathoms below the level in the Main Limestone. These were worked to within 180 fathoms of Snowdon Man on the Ellerton Moor boundary.[10] Pearson's Level (a crosscut from Devis) was being driven at this time to search for an eastern extension of the deposits worked by Raw & Co. at Devis Hole in the 1760s, but this ultimately proved fruitless. When the Kinnaird Commissioners visited the mine, some three to four hundred yards had been driven in both Robinson and Cranehow Bottom Veins, and Wellington Vein had been followed to the west. A number of rises were put up into the Red Beds Limestone from Robinson's and Cranehow Bottom Levels and a connection made to the Doctor's Level above (named after Dr Robinson, a lessee). Although Robinson and Cranehow Bottom Veins proved very poor in themselves, the associated replacement deposits, or flots, proved to be rich in the Red Beds and Main Limestones.

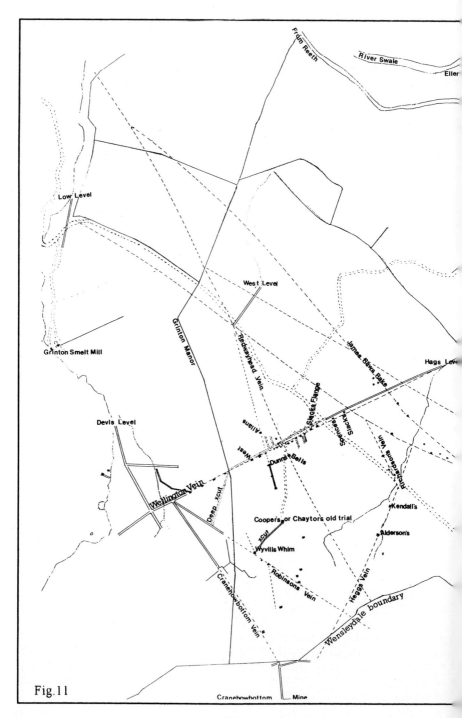

Fig.11

From Reeth

River Swale

Eller

Low Level

West Level

Grinton Manor

Redwallhead Vein

James Bows Rake

Hags Level

Grinton Smelt Mill

Devis Level

Slacks Flarge

Allans

Spencers

West

Dunnets Bells

Richardsons Vein

Kendall's

Wellington Vein

Deep xcut

Coopers or Chaytors old trial

Alderson's

xcut

Wyvills Whim

Robinsons Vein

Hags Vein

Cranehowbottom Vein

Wensleydale boundary

Cranehowbottom Mine

86

Ellerton Moor & Devis Mines

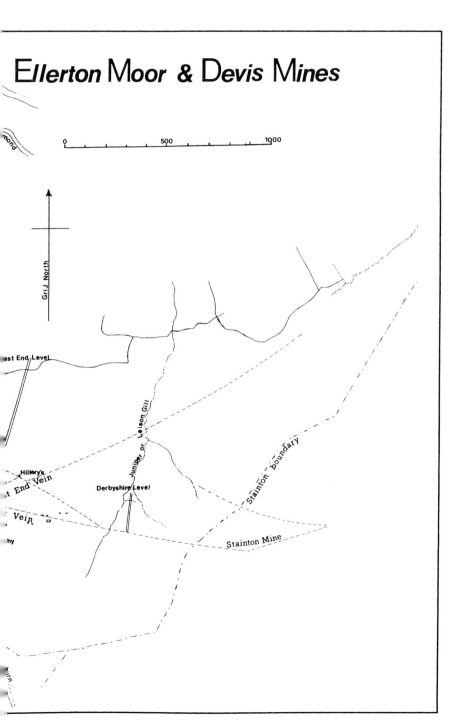

These two veins were productive on Preston Moor in Wensleydale, where they were worked from Cranehow, or Cryna, Bottom Shaft. Drives were opened in the Red Beds and had reached the Ellerton boundary at Lunton Hill by 1853.[11] The direction of the workings prompted Marmaduke Wyvill (lessee of the Ellerton Mines) to sink his whim shaft in the corner of Ellerton Moor where Cranehow Bottom and Robinson's Veins cross from Wensleydale to Grinton manor. The whim shaft was sunk onto Robinson Vein and crosscuts were made to Cranehow Bottom Vein where good ore was found in the caverns and shakes associated with it. The cost of drawing it up the shaft, however, swallowed the profit. Below Preston Moor, the drive from Cranehow Bottom Shaft ended in the top part of the Main Limestone where caverns formed a link with the Ellerton Mines.

During the sinking of Cranehow Bottom Shaft in 1806 the Swelly provided a spectacular effect, which William Sadler, the Duke of Bolton's agent, described as follows:-

> "the Cranehow bottom tryal has been one of the most singular & difficult undertakings ever here remembered, several times a day the water which is pent up bellow in large cavities in the beds, issues out of the bore hole at the shaft bottom with incredible force & rising upwards of 30 yards perpendicular falls down upon the workmen in such quantity as almost to drown them, as well as the damage of being knocked on the head with stones that it carries along with it, it generally contains some minates, at other times the bore hole is completely stopt, & detains the water for sev' days, when all is at a stand & the passage is no sooner opened with the rods than it fills up with a loose sort of gravel. Time & money are the only agents to be used & perhaps both will not have effect."

Evidently the whole ground between Cranehow Bottom and Wellington Veins was traversed by natural passages and the primary Geological Survey map shows the natural caverns to link the two mines.[12]

Although rich, the main flots below Devis Hole Level proved expensive to work. The work had to be drawn up by jack roller to Devis Level, and, owing to their dip, the beds were prone to flooding. The flots were also irregular and difficult to predict. Exploration involved following natural passages, or joints, called "Shakes", one of which opened into a "remarkable labyrinth" in 1861 and led some 440 yds beyond the Crown boundary into Ellerton Moor. Although in 1865 the mine was said to be nearly exhausted, occasional discoveries were made. One such was in December 1869 when a new flot was discovered to the west of Cranehow Bottom Vein, six fathoms below the level.[13]

The 1861 lease covenanted that a low adit be driven to drain this part of the Grinton Moor mining field with Devis Mine in mind. For this purpose, the Low Level was driven from below the Reeth to Leyburn road in Cogden Gill. By 1862 it had been driven 200 yards, but it never reached its destination and was given up in preference to Haggs Gill Level c1870.[14]

88

On Ellerton Moor, Marmaduke Wyvill must have leased this mine c1836, as his 21 year lease was said to expire on September 16th 1857. He was responsible for most of the 19th century development there, but Haggs Gill Level apparently pre-dates Wyvill's lease, and was most likely the brain child of Morley's manager, John Harland. The 1836 plan of Ellerton Moor shows the level to have been driven up under Ellerton smithy in the direction of the Grinton boundary.[15] In 1845 Wyvill bought Scott's smelting mill on Grovebeck for £50. The earliest surviving pay bills from there, dated 1854, record that he was smelting ore from Ellerton Moor.[16]

From 1854, most of Wyvill's trials were done in the Red Beds lime from Cooper's and Peacock's Shafts, with only occasional mention of Haggs Gill Level. Nearly all the ore raised was at the head price of 50 to 60 shillings per bing. That is the minimum price at which the miners could make a living wage while allowing the company a profit after handling and smelting charges and shows that all they were doing was picking over the old workings, with nothing to show in any new trials. The amount of ore raised was too small to pay for the full working of the mine, i.e. it would not cover the cost of contingencies and exploratory work.[17]

The Wyvill family had lost thousands of pounds by the spring of 1866 when they finally gave up the mine and Marmaduke Wyvill junior's letter of August 21st 1866 sums up the mood:-[18]

"I hope at all counts we shall hear nothing more of management from Edward Wyvill after the mess he and my father made in their working of the mine."

The Grinton Moor Co. had been formed to work the eastern part of Grinton Moor and in 1870 added the Ellerton ground to its own. The company began driving a deep crosscut from Haggs Gill Level to drain Devis Mine. Although Haggs Gill Level was started in the Main Limestone, the effect of the Great Stork Vein meant that the level entered the 27 Fathom Grit on the south, or downthrow, side of the vein. The exact point at which the crosscut was started is uncertain, but, judging from the *Mining Journal* reports, it was under the end of Doctor's Level (further west than indicated in fig.11) and cut Robinson Vein near Closes Sump. In 1875, when the company abandoned the mines, it was just 38 fathoms short of Robinson Vein, in the grit below the Main Lime. Official statistics record that 163 tons of lead were produced at Ellerton Moor during this period, but they probably actually came from Devis Mine.[19]

In 1888 the mines were reopened by the Grinton Mining & Smelting Company Ltd, under the management of John Rodwell Esq. This company undertook a development programme which included the clearing of Haggs Gill Level and the continuation of the Deep Crosscut. Owing to a hard bed of gritstone and the wetness of the strata, the going was difficult, but by July 5th 1890 Robinson's Vein had been cut together with a cross vein which was yielding *"nice ore"*. The cross strings continued to yield ore, if unreliably, but it was to be some time before the water above was released. On October 17th 1891, it was reported that the mines were raising nearly a ton of dressed ore per day and preparations were being made to sink into the Underset Limestone in Robinson Vein where the prospects were seen as favourable. The Official Statistics give the production from 1890 to 1892 as 99 tons. Little or no work was done after this time.[20]

Recent exploration by the Earby Mines Research Group suggests that the Deep Crosscut was of only limited value because most of the ore had already been worked out, and so its only real use was to allow free drainage, instead of the water and ore being lifted to Devis Level. Also, if reported indications of the Underset Limestone being productive were correct, then the Deep Crosscut would have been unable to drain those workings and, with hindsight, it would have been better to have continued the Low Level from Cogden Gill.

REFERENCES

1   PRO LRRO 3/85 XC4276 CL

2   NYCRO Publication & Lease 1754 ZKU/1X/41

3   NYCRO ZCC 2236 Parkes Diary

4   Ellerton Plan 1753

5   NYCRO ZQH 11/4 Mic 1166/8024

6   PRO LRRO 3/85 XC 4276 CL

7   Barker MSS Groundless assertions Morley v Harland

8   NYCRO Mic 1779/0454

9   PRO CRES 2 LRRO 1390 & ZQH 11/4 Mic 1880/Oa10

10 PRO CRES 34/213 File 1441 (2)

11 Lord Bolton's Mine Plan of Keld Heads to Cryna Bottom.

12 NYCRO ZBO IX 1/18/109

13 PRO CRES 34/213 File 1441 (2)

14 Ibid. & DHH 6/4/6

15 NYCRO ZFW 9/3 & ZFW 10/3

16 NYCRO ZFW 9/3 Mic 2037/2887

17 Ibid

18 NYCRO ZFW Mic 2037/3077

19 Burt, R. Waite, P., Atkinson, M. & Burnley, R. *The Yorkshire Mineral Statistics 1845-1913* (Exeter: Department of Economic History, University of Exeter, 1982). *Mining Journal.*

20 *Mining Journal.*

THE FREMINGTON LEAD MINES

Documentation of activities at the Fremington mines is so scarce that what small amount has survived is being presented separately.

BACKGROUND

The manor of Fremington, on the east side of Arkengarthdale, is one of the smallest in the Dales. Its southern boundary is the old Reeth to Richmond road and the eastern boundary is marked by the high moor wall which follows an ancient track known as the Wayne Way. The northern boundary is Slei Gill, with Arkle Beck as the west boundary. The main feature at Fremington is the Edge which must rank as one of the most dramatic landscapes in the Northern Dales area. This clearly shows the full range of the Main, or 12 Fathoms, and Underset Limestones.

The hub of mining activity was the Fell End area, where the Edge slopes down into Slei Gill or Farndale. In this area, early miners formed the spectacular Fell End Hushes. These worked the Wellington, Blucher, Scraes and Scatter Scar Veins, which are in turn a continuation of the North Swaledale mineral belt. Further south along the Edge, the Hyndrake and Jingle Pot Veins had some trials on them, but they both proved richer in the adjoining Marrick Liberty. The most southerly vein is at Copperthwaite, which was initially worked by hushing and later had a level driven on it. The Fremington Edge Chert mines, near Copperthwaite, were worked by the Boulder Flint Company until around 1953.

As with Grinton, the Fremington area was the scene of very early settlement with hut circles on Fremington Haggs and extensive field systems on Copperthwaite Moor dating from the second millennium B.C.[1] There was a vill here at the time of the Domesday Survey and the area was incorporated into the Honour of Richmond after 1069 and, along with Grinton, was included in the grant of Swaledale to the Gants. It was later granted by Robert de Gant to Hervey or Henry, ancestor of the Fitzhughs of Ravensworth. This grant was confirmed by King John in February 1200/1. The manor was held by the Fitzhugh family till 1512, when the estates were divided and Fremington passed to Sir Thomas Parr of Kendal. It then passed to his son, William Parr, Marquis of Northampton, but was confiscated by the Crown when he was attaindered for supporting Lady Jane Grey in 1553. He was pardoned by Queen Mary the following year and received a regrant of the manor and lead mines of Fremington, paying no rent to the Crown. Upon William Parr's death in 1571, the estates were escheated by the Crown in accordance with the conditions of the regrant.[2]

THE WHARTONS OF GILLINGWOOD

The first documented reference to mining in Fremington comes in a lease granted to Henry, Lord Scrope, and Arthur Phillips in February 1583 for the Grinton and Fremington mines.[3] The annual rental was 20 shillings which, as with Grinton, remained unchanged till 1834 when the Crown Commissioners finally accepted that they had no legal claim on the mines.

A survey of the Honours of Richmond and Middleham made in 1605 noted that Humphrey Wharton had a lease of all the mines there, apart from the Arkengarthdale mines. This lease for the Richmond and Middleham mines was renewed for a further 21 years in 1629 when Henry, Lord Scrope, came in as a partner.[4]

Humphrey Wharton belonged to a younger branch of Lord Wharton's family. Probably through this connection, he became an important Crown official in the North. He held the position of Receiver General of Land Revenues for the Archdeaconry of Richmond and for the counties of Durham and Northumberland. As such, he was ideally placed for discovering when lands or mines were available for purchase or lease. He purchased the manor of Gilling near Richmond in 1609 and built the family seat, Gillingwood Hall. In 1619 he purchased the manor of Aldbrough.[5,6] The Wharton family were to remain lessees of the mineral rights until the 19th century.

Humphrey Wharton was not averse to using his position to try and bend the law to his own ends. In 1623 he was accused by the trustees of the estates of Sir Thomas Wharton of granting himself leases and rentals of land and forests at greatly undervalued terms in an attempt to cheat Sir Thomas of his inheritance.[7]

By 1625 Wharton had built a smelt mill at the side of Slei Gill. This was mentioned in the accounts of John Hall of Storthwaite Hall, who was the Collector of the King's Rents for Fremington and Grinton. The latter recorded the following: *"Item, for work tools and for belyses about the smelting house, 30s"*.[8] A survey of the area made in 1718 shows the mill as a single building with a water wheel at one end, but by 1729 it had associated buildings, including a peat house, attached to it.[9]

In 1636 a petition was presented to the Lord Keeper by Edmund Nicholson, who had a lease of mines at Bolyhope which he had been working for the past 14 years and who had spent £1000 on development work. Humphrey Wharton, who had died the previous year, and his son, Thomas, had tried to gain possession of Nicholson's mines, but, after being defeated, the Whartons had secretly subpoenaed witnesses and procured a hearing before the Master of the Rolls at which they failed to appear. Nicholson then appealed to the King to order Thomas Wharton to appear before the Lords Justices in order that his possession be confirmed.[10]

Charles I sold the manor of Fremington to Francis Braddock and Christopher Kingscote of London for the sum of £4241 2s 3d in February 1636. This grant also contained several mines in North and South Wales, but gold and silver mines, being *"Mines Royal"*, were excepted from the grant. Mines Royal did not apply to lead mines, but confusion on this point led to their inclusion and the Crown – quite wrongly as it later appears – continued to receive rent from the Fremington mines. The following year Braddock and Kingscote sold the manor and mines to Robert Worrall and Michael Waller, and Worrall by survivorship later conveyed them to Sidney Lukyns and Richard Maddocks. The representatives of these last owners later conveyed the manor to the Freeholders, who have held it ever since.[11]

The Wharton family continued to pay the Crown the 20 shillings annual rent even though the mines were being transferred with the manor. This curious state of affairs was to continue for the next 100 years and one wonders at the motives of the Whartons and the Crown Officials who clearly had no legal right to the mines, but continued to receive rents. At no time during the Wharton tenure were duty lead payments ever specified, nor did they ever feature in returns for the Grinton Field, which was leased in tandem with Fremington.

Thomas Wharton died in 1641 and was succeeded by his son, Humphrey, who continued working the mines and paying the annual rent. A survey of the Fremington mines made during the Interregnum in 1650 valued the revenue from them at £12 per annum.[12] Humphrey Wharton expanded his mining activities into County Durham in 1660 when he obtained a lease and the position of Moormaster for the Bishop of Durham's mines for his lifetime. The wording of the grant "*as ye patents formerly ran*" suggests that Wharton had held the post previously. He was to pay the Bishop 1/9th duty. This effectively meant that he would be policing his own mines. To expand his hold on the mines further, he went to Parliament and obtained an Act enabling the Bishop to grant him the lease for three lifetimes. Anthony Wharton sold the lease to Sir William Blackett in 1696.[13]

After the Restoration, a conveyance was made of the Fremington mines on July 1st and 2nd 1667 by Luckyns and Maddocks, acting as representatives for Braddock and Kingscote. This was to confirm that Humphrey Wharton and his son, also Humphrey, were in possession of the lease of the mines.[14] After this time, no fresh lease was granted till 1696, although the Whartons continued in peaceful possession and paid the annual rent. Here again confusion reigns as the mines were not intended to be included in the original sale, yet the manorial landowners confirmed a lease.

In 1669 an attempt was made by Francis Topham, who held the vicarage of East Grinton on lease from the Crown, and Francis Atkinson, the Vicar of East Grinton, to establish that tithes were payable on ore from the Fremington mines. Humphrey Wharton and two of his miners, John Etherington and Christopher Hall, brought a case before the courts against Topham and Atkinson in the Easter Term 1669.[15] Evidence from various miners working for Wharton gives us some idea of mining at this time. The main workings were centred on Jingle Pot, Hyndrake, Fell End and Reed Gutter veins. At Copperthwaite there were two workings, one on the vein itself and the other a flot which was distinct from the vein, lying about 10 yards west of it, and worked by Etherington and Hall for the past three years. In 1659 a lessee of Topham, Richard Hutchinson of Rawcroft, had threatened to distrain the ore of Zouth Willis who was working one of the shafts at Fell End. Willis had given him a horse-load of ore and nothing had been heard of it since, till Topham made his claim. After hearing evidence from the miners, the case was found for Wharton and no tithe lead was ever paid to Grinton rectory.

The flot worked at Copperthwaite produced a large amount of ore and, as it was being worked in both manors, it became necessary to define the boundary clearly between Fremington and Marrick. Charles, Marquis of Winchester, who owned Marrick, drew up an agreement in November 1676 with Humphrey Wharton, setting out the area on the vein which Wharton could mine. Centred on the Wayne Way, an ancient high road which traverses the Edge, agreement was reached for working on three veins: Hyndrake, Jingle Pot and Copperthwaite. At Jingle Pot 150 yards was measured from the Wayne Way eastwards along the vein. Seventy-five yards of this was to belong to Marrick and the other half to Wharton. A similar arrangement was reached on the Hyndrake Vein, but the distance here was 118 yards to be divided between them. At Copperthwaite the measurements were taken from the shaft, known as the Bounder Shaft, which was worked by Hall and Etherington. Lines 25 yards long were to be taken north and south of the shaft and the ground to the west of this would be worked by the Marquis and that on the east by Wharton. By the agreement Wharton was bound to sell all the ore obtained from these veins to the Marquis *"well dressed and fit for the Smelting Harth"* at 30 shillings per bing. Boundary stones were to be set up by William Orton, acting for the Marquis, and by Phillip Wharton, acting for Humphrey Wharton.[16]

When Reginald Marriott obtained his lease of the Grinton Mines in 1697, the Fremington Mines were included, so we have the curious position whereby the Crown was collecting 20 shillings rent from Marriott, who was not working the mines, and from Anthony Wharton, who was not in possession of a lease from the Crown. The Fremington mines were again included in the renewal of Marriott's lease of Grinton in 1727 and he still continued to pay the 20 shillings rent.

Information regarding Wharton's position at Fremington emerges from evidence given in the case Marriott v Swale in 1697. Ralph Binks of Storthwaite Hall, who had worked for Thomas Wharton and his son Anthony, testified that Humphrey Wharton had purchased the mine lease from Robert Worrall. It transpired that Thomas Wharton, who succeeded the first Humphrey as Receiver of the Kings Rents for Charles I, was in arrears with the Crown for money he had received and never paid to the Crown. To avoid distraint of his and his son Humphrey's possessions, he had failed to renew the lease with the Crown as he dared not claim any lands of his own estate other than those made under old entails. The mines were still held under the original lease and, therefore, were not counted as distrainable goods.[17]

In 1729 the Farndale, or New, Mill on the side of Slei Gill was sold to Charles Bathurst who worked the Arkengarthdale Mines. The mill was owned by six partners, one of whom was Bathurst. Curiously William Wharton, who was working the mines, was not one of the partners named. The other five partners transferred their rights in the mill to Bathurst for five shillings each. The peat house and other storehouses had been purchased some time prior to this date by Bathurst.[18] The name New Mill suggests that it replaced an earlier mill, but, as there exists only the brief mention of the equipment at the first mill and nothing now remains of the site, it must continue as one of the mysteries of the Dales.

It was only in 1743, when Edmund Moore got his lease of the Grinton Mines, that the odd state of affairs was first questioned by a Grinton lessee. Moore brought an action against William Wharton in July 1743 to try and ascertain who actually owned the mines. At the trial it was stated that the Wharton family had enjoyed peaceful possession of the mines since 1628 and that the mines had never been esteemed as Mines Royal. The outcome of the case is not known, but it is likely that some arrangement was reached between Wharton and Moore. Moore demised a moiety of the Fremington mines in 1750 to Messrs Chambers and Keys.[19]

THE WHARTONS OF SKELTON CASTLE

William Wharton, the last male heir of the line, died without issue in 1746 and the family estates in Yorkshire, Westmorland and Durham, together with the mines, were divided between his three sisters. Ann, the eldest, married Ambrose Stevenson and their daughter married John Hall, of Skelton Castle, who took the surname Stevenson upon their marriage. Ann's grandson, John Hall Stevenson, adopted the surname of Wharton in 1787. This step had to be taken under the terms of the wills of Ann's other two sisters, Mary and Margaret, who had never married, in order to inherit their portion of the estates.[20]

Gillingwood Hall near Richmond, the Wharton family seat, was destroyed by a fire on December 26th 1750.[21] All papers relating to the mines were destroyed at this time, accounting for the somewhat sketchy nature of this brief history. An interesting story is attached to the fire at Gillingwood, relating to Margaret Wharton, whose ghost is said to walk the upstairs landing of a house in Thirsk. Upset that her brother William did not bequeath her the Hall, she threw a party, got drunk, and burnt it down in a fit of pique.[22]

In 1796 John Wharton of Skelton Castle and his wife, Susanna, mortgaged the Fremington Mines and their Melsonby and Aldbrough estates to Walter Fawkes, Thomas Wycliff and Thomas Swann, banker, of York. These three were then to sell the estates to clear John Wharton's debts. In 1816 an Act was passed to allow the partitioning of John Wharton's estates in Yorkshire, Westmorland and Durham.[23] He continued to receive revenue from the mines until 1827, when Thomas Swann claimed the duty lead. This action finally severed all Wharton links with the Fremington mines.[24]

A lease of the mines was granted in 1796 to Joseph Stoddart who had been working the hush named after him in Arkengarthdale.[25] As his lease from the Arkengarthdale Mineral Lords expired about this date, it is highly probable that Stoddart worked the Fell End Hushes as documentation survives to show that hushing was his main mining method.

A new lease of the mines was granted to Spence & Co. in 1814 for 14 years, during which time they raised 25,000 pieces of lead. As this company drove the Fell End Level directly on the vein, this would account for the large ore returns. John Harland, the Grinton agent, also acted as agent for these mines on behalf of John Wharton and Thomas Swann.[26]

THE SWANN BANK

In 1829 the company working the Hurst Mines took the Fremington lease and proceeded to drive the Fell End Level, which had been working up to the boundary at Wellington Whim Shaft, towards Hurst ground. In 1831 a new wheelcase was constructed at the mouth of Fell End Level and the ore dressed there was carried by Mark Peacock to the Marrick Smelt Mill at 1s 10d per bing. In the same year, Thomas Alderson and partners holed into the Hurst workings on Wellington Vein, but the life of this mine seems to have been short lived and work had ceased by 1835 after raising 3000 pieces of lead.[27]

The partners who held the Grinton Mines lease once again raised the question as to who actually owned the Fremington Mines when their lease came up for renewal in 1834. In July the Crown Solicitor reported to the Treasury Board that, after examining the Grant made to Braddock and Kingscote in 1637, he found that the whole of the mines were conveyed in the grant.[28] Under the circumstances, he recommended the omission of the Fremington Mines from the Grinton lease and thereby ended over 200 years of confusion during which time the Crown had been receiving payments for something it did not own. Whether the Wharton family had the courage to ask the Treasury for a refund is not known, but would have made a very interesting case if they had!

In January 1843 John Harland listed the iron rails in the various levels at the Fremington mines, giving a good idea of the extent of mining activity then.[29]

Iron Rails at Fell End Level	fms	ft
Smithy Level	802	0
Heggs Level	365	3
Gutters Level	468	0
Scraes Level	129	0
Copperthwaite & Jingle Pot Levels	46	0
	1810	3

The mines were next let to Owen Clough from 1862 to 1863, Arkendale Co. from 1866 to 1868 and the Fell End Mining Co. from 1869 to 1876.[30]

Sun Gutters Level, with its portal in Slei Gill Beck, had been driven 780 feet NE beneath the Main Lime some time prior to 1855 in order to try the Scatter Scar Vein, but was stopped before the vein was found. The level was later continued and the vein intersected not far from the old forehead. Rises were then put up to test it, but the vein must have been very poor at this depth and work was stopped in March 1863. In the same period, a crosscut was driven from Blucher Vein in Fell End Level to cut Black Vein, but again without finding any workable ore.

The Arkendale Co., which had a lease of the area, turned its attention to the Copperthwaite Vein at the southern end of the field. This vein had proved very rich in the Marrick Liberty and a level was started on December 2nd 1865 on top of the Five Yard Limestone. After driving through considerably slipped ground, they had put up Bells Rise to the 4th Limestone by 1868. The Copperthwaite Sun, or South, Vein was then cut and, after a rise had been made to day to ventilate the mine near the forehead, further workings were made at this horizon till the level was abandoned in March 1871.[31]

The final phase at Fell End came in May 1871 when a lease was granted by John Swann, Robert Swann of Askham Hall, Frances Elizabeth Swann, and William Clough, all of York, to the Fell End Company. This company, whose shareholders also held the Grinton mines lease, consisted of George Roper, James Robinson Tomlin, Hutton Simpson, and Richard Bowes, all of Richmond, Yorks; James Knowles and E.A. Knowles, both of Low Row; John Leonard Tomlin of South Kensington, and Joseph Brown of Oldham.

The lease for 21 years stipulated that the company was to begin immediately to drive a level from the side of Sturfitt Hall Beck in the 3rd Limestone. It was to be driven in a straight line till they cut Fell End Old Vein and then a drive was to be cut along the vein to test its productivity. The company was to employ no fewer than six men on dead work and the rent was £20 p.a., plus a duty of 1/6th of all ore raised or its cash equivalent.[32]

The Fell End Vein was reached in April 1874 after driving north for 900 feet and the East Level was then driven for 500 feet, but the vein seems to have been very poor at this depth with only a little over 30 tons of ore raised. By 1877 the company was obviously having little luck in Sturfitt Hall Level and was attempting to wriggle out of its lease by invoking the three month get-out clause. The lessors would only allow this if the company first drove a crosscut north from the level forehead for at least 80 fathoms to cut Scraes Vein. The lessors also complained that the clause respecting the number of men to be employed was not being complied with as only two men had been employed. The crosscut to find Scraes was abandoned in August 1878 after a rise was put up in the vein.[33]

The final episode for the mines occurred in November 1938 when E.M. (Fremmy) Hutchinson of Storthwaite Hall wrote to Captain Douglas, his M.P., asking him to find out who owned the mineral rights belonging to Storthwaite Hall on the Fell End Estate. Even at this late date, confusion still reigned over the mineral rights, as, in the deeds to his property, it said that the property was sold subject to clauses in the 1771 Enclosure Act saying that the minerals were reserved to the Crown. As Hutchinson wished to make a trial in the Fell End mines, he wanted to know if it would be possible to obtain a grant for opening them up.

Captain Douglas passed the letter on to the Office of Commissioners for Crown Lands, who passed it on to the Mines Department. Their reply is given verbatim: *"I suggest the answer to the present enquiry might be simply that many years ago the lead mines of Fremington were included in leases of lead mines in Yorks granted by the Crown but Crown claims to Fremington was abandoned in 1834 in favour of a claim by the Lord of the Manor and we have no information as to who is the present owner"*.[34]

This situation still stands at the present date and even now ownership of the mines belongs, as far as the author knows, to no one. Anyone like a mine?

REFERENCES

1 Spratt. D. & Burgess. C. (eds). *Upland Settlement in Britain* (British Archaeological Review, British Series 143, 1985). Laurie. T.C. Early land division and settlement in Swaledale and on the eastern approaches to the Stainmore Pass over the North Pennines. pp.137, 140, 145, 156.

2 V.C.H. Fremington. p.240.

3 PRO. CRES 34/211. File 1441, LRRO 3/85.

4 Willan. T.S. & Crossley. E.W.*Three Seventeenth Century Yorkshire Surveys* (Leeds: YAS, Record Series Vol.104, 1941), p.88, 149.

5 Speight, H. *Romantic Richmondshire* (London, 1897) p.175.

6 Surtees, R. *History of Durham* Vol 1. p.108.

7 YML. Hailstone MSS. Box 4. Bundle 32.

8 Barker MSS. Tyson. L.O. *A History of the Manor & Lead Mines of Arkengarthdale, Yorkshire* (Sheffield: NMRS, British Mining No.29, 1986) p.20.

9 NYCRO. ZQX. Mic 2023/321-335.

10 PRO. State Papers Domestic. 1636.

11 PRO. CRES 34/211. VCH. Fremington. p.240.

12 PRO. Exchequer Depositions. E137/26.

13 Proceedings of the Society of Antiquaries, Newcastle upon Tyne, 3rd Series, Vol.1 (1903/04). My thanks to Ray Fairbairn for passing on this information.

14 PRO. CRES 34/211.

15 PRO. Exchequer Depositions. E134. 21 Chas II. Easter 9. Wharton of Skelton Castle MSS.

16 NYCRO. ZAZ. Mic 1288. Tyson. L.O. *A History of the Manor & Lead Mines of Marrick, Swaledale* (Sheffield: British Mining No.38, 1989) pp.24f.

17 PRO. Exchequer Depositions. E134. 9 Will 3rd. Trinity 18.

18 NYCRO. ZQX. 2/1/1.

19 PRO. CRES 34/211.

20 Graves, Rev. J. *History of Cleveland* (1808), p.359. Orde, J.W. *The History & Antiquities of Cleveland* (London, 1846), pp.253-258. NYCRO. ZDO 10.

21 Wilson, Thomas (of Leeds). *The North Riding of York. A Collection of the Coats of Arms and descents of the several families of the Nobility & Gentry*. YML. Add. Man. 164/3.

22 Waterson. E. & Meadows. P. *Lost Houses of York and the North Riding* (Bridlington: Clifford Warde & Co, 1990) p.47.

23 NYCRO. ZDO. 10. An Act for effecting an exchange of certain settled estates of John Wharton Esquire, for other estates belonging to him in Fee Simple in the Counties of York, Westmorland, and Durham, 1816.

24 PRO. CRES 2/1390.

25 Tyson, L.O.*Arkengarthdale*. pp.24-26.

26 PRO. CRES 2/1390

27 NYCRO. Coates MSS.

28 PRO. CRES 2/1390.

29 NYCRO. Coates MSS.

30 Burt, R., Waite, P., Atkinson, M. and Burnley, R. *The Yorkshire Mineral Statistics 1845-1913* (Exeter: Department of Economic History, University of Exeter, 1982), p.26.

31 Abandonment Plan. 1886.

32 DRO. D/HH/6/4/102.

33 DRO. D/HH/6/4/108.

34 PRO. CRES 1441/3.

OTHER MINERALS

COAL MINING AT GRINTON

Coal seams in the Grassington Grits were worked on Preston Moor, in the Bolton Royalty, and at the Grinton Moor Colliery as far back as 1768. These pits, which were leased and worked separately from the lead mines, produced poor coal, however, and their primary function was to supply the Grinton smelt mill.

Two drifts opposite the Summer Lodge smelt mill worked a poor quality coal for lime burning. These drifts, and some shafts just inside Summer Lodge Moor at the Windgates Colliery, were leased by J.C.D. Charlesworth to Edward Broderick of Spring End in 1860, in exchange for shooting and fishing rights in the enclosed lands on Summer Lodge Moor.[1] The inventory of mine plant taken before Charlesworth purchased the mines, lists Broderick's coal level as having 60 fms of rail laid down.[2] This arrangement lasted till 1895 when Luther Broderick, a chartered accountant from Manchester and a descendant of Edward Broderick, fought a lengthy legal dispute with A.H. Charlesworth. Broderick was seeking to re-establish his shooting rights on Summer Lodge Moor and this, the last great law suit fought at Grinton, continued a long tradition, but with no violent acts.[3]

STONE MINING AT GRINTON

Sandstone for roofing and gritstone for house building have been worked at several places in Grinton.

WHITASIDE QUARRY   SD993973

This quarry was in a long outcrop of grit above the Five Yard Limestone. It had a working face of about 5 to 7 feet in height and about 170 yards in length and provided good building stone used on many of the houses along Birks Side.

LOW HARKERSIDE QUARRY (LEVEL)   SE028978

This quarry was included in a Redemption Certificate for Land Tax in 1877 and The List of Mines shows two people working it in 1904.[4,5] In April 1905 it was leased by A.H. Charlesworth to William Pedley of the Half Moon Hotel at Grinton for 10 years at £5 p.a. rent.[6] William, a building contractor, only worked it when he needed roofing flags. He worked with his son, Edward, until February 21st 1910, when, whilst working alone, his legs were crushed in a rock fall. Although he managed to drag himself to the entrance, he died there from loss of blood. Edward, who never spoke to his children about the accident, kept the lease on until 1920, but the level was never worked again.[7]

REFERENCES

1 Barker MSS. Charlesworth v Broderick.

2 Holliday MSS.

3 Barker MSS. Charlesworth v Broderick.

4 Holliday MSS.

5 *List of Mines in Great Britain* (London: HMSO - various years)

6 Holliday MSS.

7 The late Elsie Pedley of Grinton, pers comm; Edward Pedley of Northallerton, pers comm; Lawrence Barker, pers comm.

THE SMELT MILLS

Owing to the scant documentary references for the smelt mills in Grinton, it has been decided that treating them separately is the most expedient manner in which to develop a likely sequence of events. The Grinton smelt mills were first described by Raistrick in 1975 and later, in 1992, by Gill.[1,2] During research for this monograph, a little more information has come to light and a reassessment of their work has become necessary.

HOW OR LOW MILL   SE049964

No actual date is known for the building of this, the first smelt mill at Grinton. When Reginald Marriott purchased the surface rights for the wastes at Grinton from the Hillary family in 1705 and 1710, he also obtained ownership of all quarries and turbary rights and the coal mines in the wastes.[3] This would surely have prompted him to build the first mill in the Grinton mining field. Prior to this date, documentary evidence shows that he had been using the Duke of Bolton's Mill at Marrick in 1697, the Marrick Cupola in 1704, and possibly also the nearby Ellerton and Bobscar Mills.[4]

Situated on the east side of Cogden Beck, the site for the new mill was eminently suitable because of the regular water supply. It was also well situated for the mines which were being developed by Marriott on Grinton How. Fuel could be provided from the pits on Coal Pit Moor, near the southern boundary, and peat was also in plentiful supply near the pits. Stone could be provided from his quarries, so he had an ideal opportunity to build his own mill and operate it at minimal cost.

A map of the manor made in 1768 shows the mill as a single building with the chimney at the southern end. A separate building alongside would have been the peat store and there were two reservoirs to supply the waterwheel.[5]

The first documented reference to a mill occurs in the mine accounts for 1722/3.[6] The next reference can be found in 1733 when the mill and utensils were included in the proposed sale to the London Lead Company by Hugh Marriott.[7]

When Hugh Marriott demised the mine lease to Edmund Moore in 1736, the smelt mill was excepted and retained as part of his estate at Grinton until sold by his wife to Caleb Readshaw in May 1756. This sale included "*the smelting mill with a little house or chamber and backside thereunto*". The mill was included as part of Readshaw's marriage settlement drawn up in the same month.[8]

By this time, the mineral lease had passed to the Moore family from Devon and, in 1759, Mrs Frances Moore became involved in a dispute over smelting her lead at the mill owned by Caleb Readshaw.[9] This gives some idea of the difficulties experienced by the Crown lessees not owning their own mill, thereby being at the mercy of the owner of the wastes and mill. Leases granted to sub-lessees state that she was bound to find a smelt mill for their ore, otherwise she had to pay three shillings towards smelting costs.[10] One possible cause of the above dispute could

Plate 6. How smelt mill, looking north-east. (R.F. White, 1995).

be that Readshaw may have built a slag hearth at the mill and this entailed greater costs for smelting than at the regular hearth. This theory can be supported by the fact that the first leases granted in 1758 contained the proviso that Mrs Moore was to have possession of all slag lead left over after smelting at the ore hearth. In 1761 the wording of the leases changed and the Adventurers were to be allowed a share of the slag lead after smelting at the slag hearth. This is the first mention of a slag hearth, which might suggest that Readshaw had built one at the mill between 1758 and 1759. By the terms of the lease *"the refuge or waste at the mill to be run at the slag hearth by the said partnership and when done Mrs Moore to have half of the lead so smelted at the slag hearth which is called Pig and Pig"*. After this date, all leases granted include the pig and pig clause.[11]

In the winding up accounts, prior to the new lease being granted in 1776, the work utensils at the How Mill were valued at £60 3s 7d.[12] A survey made by George Jackson prior to the new lease contains a clause which mentions that the Crown lessees have a lease of the mills till May Day 1775.[13] This suggests that Readshaw, who had recently become a shareholder in the mines, leased out the mill rather than working it himself.

When Caleb Readshaw Morley (grandson of the Caleb who had purchased from Mrs Moore) was declared bankrupt in 1791, the Court of Chancery ordered him to sell off the manor to pay his debts. The highest bidders were James Fenton, of Loversall near Wakefield, and Edward Wilkinson, of Potterton near York, who

Plate 7. How smelt mill and peat house, looking west
down line of flue. (R.F. White, 1995).

became the new Manorial Lords. Included in the schedule of Readshaw's property
at Grinton was the *"Smelting Mill and other buildings on the wastes"*. Neither
of these two ever became actively involved with the mines and purchased the
unenclosed land solely for the sporting rights. In 1803 Fenton & Wilkinson sold
the wastes, smelt mill and other holdings to Christopher and Mathew Whitelock
of Cogden Hall. The Whitelock family were shareholders at Grinton and other
mines in the area. After a dispute over shooting rights on Summer Lodge Moor,
the Whitelocks transferred back to Fenton and Wilkinson all the estate apart from
the smelt mill which they retained and, as will be shown below, rebuilt.[14]

From 1820 to 1822 ore from the Grinton mines was sent to other mills in the manor
and also in other mineral liberties. This gives the probable date for the How Mill

being extensively rebuilt and the flue added.[15] This is backed up in a report made by the Crown Agent, John Bower, in 1830 which mentions that Messrs Robinson, Whitelock & Co. had, in the expectation of rich finds at the Grinton mines which they were sub-leasing, recently erected a new smelting mill on the waste.[16]

No more is heard of the mill till the Crown's sale of the mineral rights to Charlesworth in 1876.[17] The remaining parties to the 1857 lease declined to renew it and sold the mine plant to Charlesworth. It included the following:-[18]

ELLERTON & GRINTON MOOR MINE PLANT - 1876

> Smelt Mill.
> 250 loads of peat.
> 2 Ore Hearths, Slag Hearth & Furnace.
> Bellows, Weighing Beam etc.
> Water Wheel, Spur Wheel & Crank.
> 4 metal rollers, spindles & levers.

In the prospectus for the Grinton Mining & Smelting Co. Ltd, issued in 1888, John Rodwell, the agent, wrote that the mill had two Scotch Hearths, a slag hearth, roasting furnace, three waterwheels, bellows etc which required some repair to put them in working order.[19] Reports by Rodwell to the *Mining Journal* in July and September 1890 state that repairs to the smelt mill were completed. These

Plate 8. How smelt mill, east side, showing egress of flue. (R.F. White, 1995).

included the erection of a new Scotch Hearth, slag hearth and roasting furnace which took less than half the amount of water than had been needed to drive the large waterwheel for blast purposes.[20] The *Craven Herald* in 1892 reported the refurbishment of the mill and noted that a long length of new flue had been built (repaired?).[21] The Grinton Mining & Smelting Co. Ltd was officially dissolved in December 1895 and the mill was never used for smelting again.

THE GROVEBECK SMELT MILLS
Roughly a mile further west from Cogden Gill is Grovebeck Gill, a strong stream upon which three separate smelt mills were eventually built. Sadly these mills are now ruined and most of the stonework has been removed. The sequence of mill building at Grovebeck is made more complicated as the smelting site is often simply referred to as Grovebeck Mill long after the first mill was derelict.

GROVEBECK MILL   SE028970
The mines at Grovebeck and Harkerside were extensively developed after 1761 when the area was blocked out for leasing to three sets of adventurers, Robert Elliott, John Simpson, and Thomas Dunne.[22] These were the first people to develop this area in an intensive manner and, as such, would have raised large amounts of ore which the How Mill was probably incapable of handling. This fact alone would have convinced the sub-lessees that they would need their own mill. Another influential factor would be that they would no longer have to pay Mrs Moore, the Crown lessee, for smelting their ore.

A survey of the Grinton Mines made in 1768 by George Jackson shows the Grove Beck smelt mill in the area leased to John Simpson & Co.[23] It can be reasonably assumed that the Grovebeck mill was built by Simpson or it could have been a joint venture with the other two adventurers who were working the area after 1762.

NEW MILL   SE030971
This mill was 550 metres downstream from Grove Beck Mill, but no documentation ever refers to it. Its only occurrence is on maps. It was shown on Teesdale's map of 1828, on an 1848 map of Grinton and as a ruin on the 1854 O.S. map.[24]

SCOTT'S MILL   SE031972
This was the longest lived of the Grovebeck mills. John Scott of Reeth, who built it, was embroiled in the dispute over ownership of the Beldi Hill Mines, which he leased. Up to 1769 he smelted ore from those mines at the Spout Gill Mill, but then he was prevented from using the mill when it was taken over by Lord Pomfret's agents.[25] Scott could use no other mill so he built one at Grovebeck where he was a partner. William Chaytor mentions in a letter dated 1771 that he had been told that John Scott, a shopkeeper of Reeth, had "*smelted at the Grovebeck Mill to the letter Z*".[26] This is evidence that the mill was built between 1769 and 1771.

The Crown lease of the Grinton Mines expired in 1774. Accounts made in the handing over period at the end of the lease mention that the utensils at the "*New Mill*" were valued at £59 18s 11d.[27] The new lessees for the block in which the mill was situated were Fowler Hickes & Co. Scott was one of the partners.[28] As the Crown lessees did not own the surface rights, the mill must have been built under licence from Caleb Readshaw. This is borne out by a later sale of the mill.

When the How Mill was being rebuilt in 1820/22, ore was smelted at Scott's mill, although it is referred to as Grove Beck Mill. Scott's Mill was sold by John Bailey Langhorne of Reeth, one of the partners in the Grinton Moor Company, to Marmaduke Wyvill in March 1845. The mill then contained an ore hearth, slag hearth, roasting furnace, waterwheel and utensils.[29] Wyvill, who was working the Ellerton mines, smelted his ore at this mill till 1857. It was shown on the 1854 O.S. map as a long narrow building about 21 feet by 70 feet.

In 1866 it was smelting ore from the Whitaside mines.[30] The last notice of the mill comes in February 1877 when it was included in a Redemption Certificate for Land Tax paid by J.C.D. Charlesworth.[31] As the mill had no flue, it could not have smelted very efficiently, but, as it continued to be used over a lengthy period, it must have been economically more expedient to use this mill than any other.

SUMMER LODGE MILL   SD966950

This, the most westerly of the Grinton Mills, was built to serve the Summer Lodge Mines. The veins at Summer Lodge were first discovered in the 1770s but, owing to disputes over the boundary, were not intensively worked till 1810. After this date, large quantities of ore were raised from the newly developed veins. In July 1810 the Crown's Duty Lead amounted to £1650 and there were another 300 tons unsmelted on the bank.[32] Such production would fully justify the company building its own mill. A map attached to a letter written in March 1812 by Thomas Butson, the Grinton mine agent, shows the New (Summer Lodge) Mill.[33] This and production data dates the building of the mill as sometime in 1811. Construction of the mill and of two miles of road at a cost of between £700 and £800 were undertaken by Josias Readshaw Morley & Co. He was one of the Crown lessees, but had a share in Summer Lodge. During the period from 1811 to 1817, the mill produced 41,117 pieces of lead.[34]

The mill was still in work during the period when the How Mill was being rebuilt in 1820 to 1822 as it was one of the mills named as smelting Grinton ore.[35] The Ordnance Survey of 1854 shows it as a smelt mill, rather than as an old mill, which indicates it was not a ruin. When Charlesworth purchased the mine plant in 1876, the grinding mill, smithy and dressing floors were complete, but no mention is made of a smelt mill as at the How Mill.[36] This can be taken as an indication that the mill was either derelict or dismantled. Sadly, very little now remains as its proximity to the road makes it an ideal quarry for building stone.

ELLERTON MILL   SE069976

Very little is known about this mill or who built it. The first notice of it comes in 1682, when Lord Wharton sent ore there for smelting and it was noted as having an ore hearth and slag hearth.[37] It is possible that Grinton ore was smelted there for Reginald Marriott before he built the How Mill.

In 1754 Henry Drax leased the Ellerton Mines and the smelt mill to William Sutton, lead merchant of Stockton, and Ralph Hutchinson, land agent of Richmond. They purchased the mill utensils from Drax for £38 11s 6d.[38] It is also shown on Jackson's map of 1768.[39]

REFERENCES

1 Raistrick, A. *The Lead Industry of Wensleydale & Swaledale, Volume 2 - The Smelt Mills* (Hartington: Moorland, 1975).

2 Gill. M.C. Yorkshire Smelting Mills Part 1: The Northern Dales *British Mining*, No.45 (1992), pp.111-150.

3 Barker MSS. Charlesworth v Broderick.

4 PRO. LRRO 3/85. Tyson, L.O.*A History of the Manor & Lead Mines of Marrick, Swaledale* (Sheffield: British Mining No.38, 1989), p.26.

5 PRO. MPE 531. MPE 390.

6 PRO. LRRO 3/85.

7 NRO. London Lead Company Minute Book. LLC/7.

8 PRO. CRES 2/1390. NYCRO. ZHP. Mic 1324. DRO. D/HH/6/4/2. YML. Hailstone MSS. Box 5. File 41.

9 NYCRO. ZHP Mic 1324.

10 NYCRO. ZKU.

11 NYCRO. ZKU.

12 PRO. LRRO. 3/85.

13 PRO. CRES 2/1390.

14 Barker MSS. Charlesworth v Broderick.

15 PRO. LR 5/9.

16 PRO. CRES 2. LRRO. 1390.

17 PRO. CRES 34/214.

18 Holliday of Mount St John MSS.

19 Barker MSS.

20 *Mining Journal*. 1890, 5th July, p.775; 1890, 20th September, p.1099.

21 NMRS Records - *Craven Herald*. 1892, 16th September Page 3, column 6.

22 NYCRO. ZKU.

23 PRO. MPE.351. MPE.390.

24 Gill, *Yorkshire Smelting Mills: Part 1*. pp.130-131. Raistrick, *Smelting Mills*, p.60.

25 ibid. p.123 & p.56

26 NYCRO. ZCC 2183.

27 PRO. CRES 2. LRRO 1390.

28 PRO. LRRO 34/214.

29 PRO. LR 5/9. Gill, *Yorkshire Smelting Mills: Part 1*. p.131. Raistrick, *Smelting Mills*, p.62. NYCRO. ZFW 7/4 & ZFW 9/3.

30 Raistrick, *Smelting Mills*, p.62. Barker MSS. Notebook of Adam Barker.

31 Holliday MSS.

32 PRO. LR 5/9.

33 PRO. CRES 2/1390.

34 PRO. CRES 2/1390.

35 PRO. LR 5/9.

36 Holliday MSS.

37 NYCRO. RQR 9/83 and 9/108. Gill, *Yorkshire Smelting Mills: Part 1*. p.132. Raistrick, *Smelting Mills*, p.33.

38 NYCRO. ZKU. 1X/41 & 1X/42. Hornshaw, T.R. *Copper Mining at Middleton Tyas* (Northallerton: NYCRO, Publication 6, 1975), p.59.

39 PRO. MPE 531 & MPE 390.

THE GRINTON HOW OR LOW MILL COMPLEX

In its present form the Grinton smelt mill complex comprises a T-shaped smelt mill building, rectangular peat store, horizontal flue, the foundations of two rectangular buildings, a series of trackways and water management earthworks. The buildings are sited on the east bank of Lemon Gill and are positioned so as to make use of a major spring in the bed of the beck some 65 metres to the south of the mill. They occupy two narrow terraces, some 25 metres and 20 metres wide, both of which are probably part natural in origin but modified by man. The beck is dammed by a low earth and stone bank, now partly breached, 57½ metres south east of the mill building. It is partially culverted below this dam. Culverting the beck created a level working area to the north, west and south of the mill. The Peat House (store) lies on the higher of the two terraces, 4½ metres above the mill. At the eastern edge of this terrace cross two north-south trending tracks. The 333 metre (1100 foot) long horizontal flue left the mill at about the height of the Peat House terrace. It ran along the south side of the Peat House, under the principal track, before gently rising to a small chimney on Sharrow Hill at 387 metres, or 1210 feet OD. Only the outline of the base of this chimney now survives.

THE MAP EVIDENCE
Unlike most of the lead smelting mills in the Yorkshire Dales the complex, although two kilometres from Grinton, the nearest village, was sufficiently close to domestic buildings to have been surveyed at 1:2500 (25 inches to one mile) scale by the Ordnance Survey (OS) in 1891. The published 1:2500 County Series maps of 1893 and 1913 provide important evidence concerning the layout of the mill complex and complement the 1856 1:10,560 (6") scale OS map and the 1774 Grinton Manor estate map and a rather less detailed 1768 map.[1]

The 1774, 1856 and 1893 maps all show a building between the present mill and peat house, aligned at right angles to the flue (figs 5 & 12). There is now only slight field evidence for the existence of this building, but the 1913 map shows the complex in essentially its present form (fig.13). The 1856 and 1893 maps both show the flue, called a 'tunnel' in 1856, extending to the top of Sharrow Hill where a chimney is named in 1893 but not in 1856. No flue is shown on the 1774 map although the detail immediately to the south of the Peat House is indistinct.

PREVIOUS STUDIES
The Grinton Mill and Peat House formed part of Robert Clough's seminal study of the buildings, or more specifically the smelt mills and to a lesser extent, peat stores, of the lead industry of the Yorkshire Dales. His 1948 drawings of Grinton Mill, in part reconstructions, were first published in the journal *Cave Science* and were brought to the attention of a wider, though still limited, public by his privately produced opus, "*The Lead Smelting Mills of the Yorkshire Dales: Their Architectural Character, Construction and Place in the European Tradition*".[2,3,4] This book has been the foundation of much of the subsequent activity in the investigation and conservation of the above ground remains of the Yorkshire lead mining industry.

Plate 9. The now demolished building near the How smelt mill. (YDNP, 1963)

Plate 10. The now demolished building near the How smelt mill. (Barker, c1963)

According to the published list of subscribers, two copies of the first edition were purchased by the Ministry of Works, the body then responsible for the formal protection of historic buildings and monuments through the listed building and scheduled ancient monument procedures. Nevertheless Grinton was not one of the first lead industry sites in the Yorkshire Dales to receive statutory protection. The hexagonal Old Powder House in Arkengarthdale was included on the statutory list of buildings of special architectural or historic interest in 1966 and was followed, in 1969, by the Old Gang Smelting Mill and Peat House and the Marrick Lead Smelting Mills.[5]

Meanwhile the Grinton buildings continued to be used, unlike most lead industry buildings in the Yorkshire Dales, albeit for agricultural purposes. The Peat House was used for hay storage and as a sheep shelter, while the mill building contained a sheep dip, dating from 1924. By the 1970s, however, the buildings were suffering from neglect and there were fears that they might meet the same fate as the two storey structure which had stood to the south of the mill. This was derelict, though still standing, in the early 1960s (plates 9 & 10), but was subsequently quarried away as a source of ready worked building stone.

In the early 1970s the North Riding National Park Committee began to take an interest in the remains of the lead industry. A preliminary survey was carried out by the North Riding Planning Department. This identified some of the principal remains, their condition and possible uses. A report, which suggested Grinton as a suitable site for possible development as a museum/interpretive centre, was considered by the North Riding National Park Committee prior to any formal discussion with landowners. The concept of protecting and interpreting some remains of the industry attracted the interest of the press and thus the landowner at Grinton and his agent first heard about the proposal through the local newspaper coverage. They were understandably displeased! Because of this, and the then forthcoming local government reorganisation, the principal proposals were put into abeyance.

Building Preservation Notices, however, were served in 1972 on the remains at Grinton, and at the Surrender Lead Smelting Mill, six kilometres to the west, to ensure that no further deliberate demolition for building stone occurred. These notices were confirmed by the Secretary of State and the buildings were added to the Statutory List of Buildings of Special Architectural or Historic Interest in February 1973. 'Listing' however did not reduce the rate of natural decay. In 1975 Grinton Mill and Peat House, including the flue but not the dams or associated earthworks, were formally designated a scheduled ancient monument (North Yorkshire 1166) and this provided an impetus for consolidation works.

THE BUILDINGS

The mill is a well built, substantial structure of coursed sandstone rubble, with large, squared quoins bearing clear tool marks. The roof, carried centrally over the whole building, is of local stone slates although the diminishing coursing varies over the two parts of the T-shaped building. This unconformity predates the 1987 re-roofing. The timber trusses are impressive and much other timberwork also survives, mostly associated with the bellows frame and with an overhead launder for the overshot waterwheel. Timber doorposts and lintels survive. They are much scored by recent graffiti, but some also bear well-formed letters, eg GH, which seem to have been branded into the wood. These letters may date from the working life of the mill or from its subsequent agricultural use. The original floor is not visible. Clough's 1948 survey indicates flagstones, but these may be hypothetical or have been subsequently robbed. The floor is now formed of rich organic earth deriving from the building's use as an animal shelter and from occasional flooding.[6]

The smelt mill has two main rooms: the furnace room, 15 metres wide on the south side, with the smaller bellows room, about eight metres wide, abutting to the north (fig.14). They are separated by two structures. The northernmost is the real cross-wall, pierced by a broad arch, 5.7 metres wide and 3.45 metres high, which gives access to the curving dividing wall which forms the backs of the range of (originally) three hearths.

The furnace room is entered by three doors, in the centre of the south side (where part of the threshold survives) and at the southern ends of the east and west walls. There are two equally spaced windows in the south side. The centre of the area in front of the hearths is occupied by a sheep dip, built by Mr T. Brown of Swale

Plate 11. How smelt mill: remains of masonry arch for an ore-hearth with hole for tuyère in back wall and flue outlet above. (R.F. White, 1995).

110

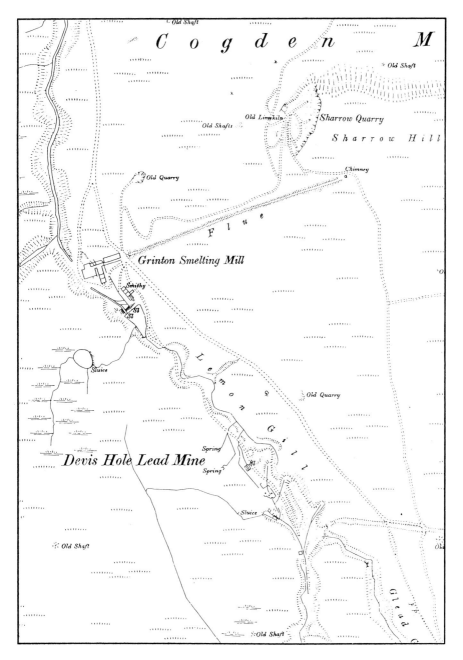

Fig.12. Ordnance Survey 1/2500 sheet. Surveyed in 1891 and published 1893.

Plate 12. How smelt mill: timber frame for the blowing
system. (R.F. White, 1995).

Hall in 1924, with a concrete floor and low side walls. The western of these walls
abuts the main hearth wall and is entirely modern, but the eastern incorporates part
of the dividing wall between the central and eastern hearths. The sheep dip makes
use of a narrow door leading to the north half of the building, but examination of
the surrounding mortar and the use of firebricks indicate that this is not an original
access between the hearths and the bellows house.

Enough of the western hearth survives to give an impression of its final form. The
back is pierced, off centre, by a large square opening, 0.7 metre by 0.63 metre, just
above present floor level, a tuyère hole for the bellows housed in the northern part
of the building, and, near ground level, by a smaller opening, 0.17 metre by 0.23
metre, which may have been for a separate forced air flow to a sumpter pot. A low
stone bench and a thick sandstone slab standing on edge, on either side of the

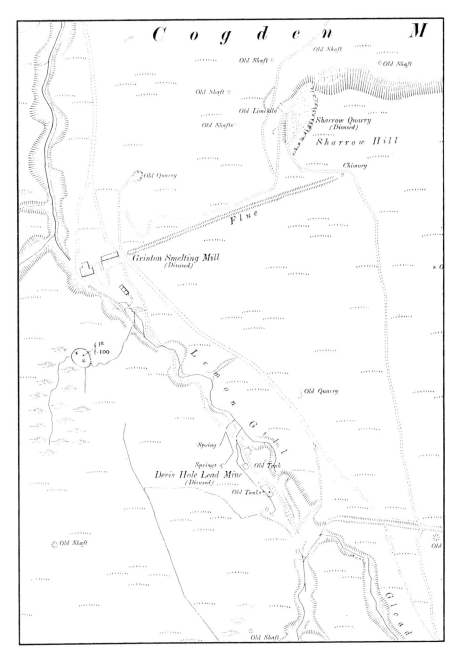

Fig.13 Ordnance Survey 1/2500 sheet. Revised in 1910 and published 1913.

Plate 13. How smelt mill: launder and bearings on timber above the frame for the blowing system. (R.F. White, 1995).

tuyère hole, are interpreted as the remains of the supports of an ore hearth. This was originally set in an arched alcove, the stonework partially supported by iron tie bars and circular pattrass plates. The remains of the alcove can still be seen abutting the west wall. The walling here is discoloured by soot from a recent fire.

Behind the hearth, at 2.85 metres above present floor level, runs the horizontal flue. The arched mouth of the flue is 1.2 metres wide and 1.7 metres high, narrowing to one metre wide towards the east. There is no apparent evidence of lead fume or heat discoloration on its walls. The junction with the flue(s) from the central and eastern hearth has been destroyed. The north wall of this flue abuts the dividing cross wall of the two parts of the mill building; the south wall abuts a second, parallel, dividing wall which rises from the, now mainly destroyed, vaulting of the tops of the hearths. Unlike the northern wall, this latter wall does not rise the full height of the building but only to the level of the uppermost purlin. The space above the flue between these walls is 2.15 metres wide, but does not appear to have been used. The rubble packing the sides of the flue is not tied into the cross walls, but this was probably to allow heat expansion rather than indicating a subsequent insertion.

The two side-walls dividing the three hearths survive, though each now ends in broken masonry and the original layout of the eastern and central hearth is not certain. Clough shows a 'storeroom' in the eastern side of the mill occupying most

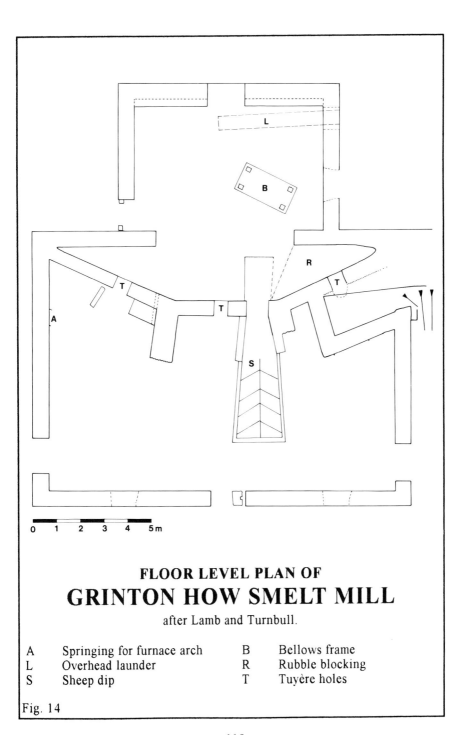

FLOOR LEVEL PLAN OF
GRINTON HOW SMELT MILL
after Lamb and Turnbull.

A	Springing for furnace arch	B	Bellows frame
L	Overhead launder	R	Rubble blocking
S	Sheep dip	T	Tuyère holes

Fig. 14

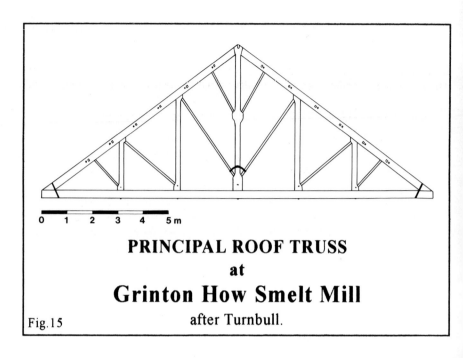

PRINCIPAL ROOF TRUSS
at
Grinton How Smelt Mill
Fig.15   after Turnbull.

of the site of the easternmost furnace. The western wall of this clearly abuts the rear wall. It is of one build with the main part of the south wall of the '*store room*'; the position at the eastern end of the south wall is less clear. Here the south wall is partly tied into the eastern wall of the furnace room, matching that on the opposite side of the room, but there is also a probable rebuilding line, or slight subsidence, in the south wall itself. The position has been confused by repointing, and possibly partial rebuilding, in the 1970s. The base of the southern face of the wall incorporates some brickwork and the remains of four, one inch diameter, threaded iron rods, one broken off at the wall. Four putlog holes and five firebricks are incorporated higher up in the wall; Lamb (pers com) has pointed out the similar positioning of the brick and iron work to the slag hearth shown by Percy and suggests that Clough's '*store room*' wall incorporates the remains of a slag hearth.[7] J.L. Barker (pers com) suggests that this is the remains of a roasting hearth. The latter could have made use of a short vertical chimney rather than the long horizontal flue. Insertion of such a chimney may have been responsible for the weakening of the roof timbers and covering which necessitated the 1977 consolidation works. There is no apparent access to this 'store room'; the blocking may therefore represent the sealing off of a redundant or ruined furnace. A new Scotch Hearth, slag hearth and roasting furnace are mentioned in 1890, while two Scotch Hearths, a slag hearth and a roasting furnace are mentioned in 1888 (above, 103). A cast iron workstone, some 0.91 by 0.44 by 0.095 metres has recently been recognised by J.L. Barker in Reeth. It was unearthed in the garden of a house formerly belonging to John Barker, agent for the Grinton estate for about 40 years until his death in 1960, and may well have come from Grinton Mill.

116

The roof of the furnace-house is supported on two identical, well carpentered, timber king-post tie beams with angle struts trusses. The tie beams are 0.28 by 0.165 metres in section. All of the long timbers are single pieces, with no scarfing or other joining of shorter lengths. All joints appear to be forms of mortice-and-tenon. Vertical members are additionally bolted to the main horizontal beam and there are a few additional bolts, as well as wrought-iron straps at the basal corners of the main truss and between the king-post and the lower central pair of angle struts (fig.15). The purlins are each pegged into the rafters.

The narrow space between the furnace backs and the true cross-wall may have been solely used to carry the trunking from the bellows to the tuyères. This would have more or less filled the space. At the acute angles at the east and west ends, the slightly corbelled roof drops virtually to floor level to support the weight of the flue overhead. The open ends are supported by timber lintels at the western side and by a timber lintel and iron rails on the east. The latter lintel is slightly larger than the western lintel and does not include any nails or other fixings. The western side remains accessible, though the eastern is blocked to breast height by carefully packed rubble.

The northern part of the building, the bellows room, is today entered by a door at the southern end of the west side and by another, in the centre of the north side, although this latter, possibly a later insertion, has also later been at least partially blocked. There is a window on the eastern side. A low, 0.28 metre wide stone

Plate 14. How smelt mill during re-roofing. (R.F. White, 1987).

117

'*bench*' runs along the northern wall. A timber channel or duct, entering by an opening in the east wall 4.2 metres above present floor level, provided water for a now vanished overshot wheel. There is no surface trace of the internal wheel-pit or of the bearings for the waterwheel and thus it is not possible without excavation to ascertain its size. The wheel is, however, likely to have been some 5½ to 6½ metres in diameter and about half a metre wide. The tail race has not been positively identified, but its position is most likely to be represented by the depression by the beck and change of angle of the training wall north west of the mill building. There is a leat leading into the east side of the culverted section of beck (S. Bassham pers com), but this seems too far upstream to be the tail race from the present mill and may relate to earlier use of the site.

The bellows room is dominated by the massive timber frame which supported the blowing mechanism itself. One corner of a concrete base is visible under the earth and muck which cover the floor. The timbers are tied in to the south wall of the bellows room above the arch. Raistrick suggested that the timber framework was for a blowing engine and shows a redrawn illustration from the London Lead Company's Minute Books.[8] He suggested that the awkward relationship of waterwheel and timberwork is due to the need to fit the mechanism into an existing building. This, however, does not fit the documentary or physical evidence. Lamb discusses the design and efficiency of blowing engines and suggests that a blowing engine as shown by Raistrick would have been technically primitive by 1822 and incapable of providing a sufficient blast for three hearths.[9] Woodall has also commented on a bracket, positioned to take an upward thrust, on one of the principal uprights of the timber frame and suggests that this is evidence for bellows, positively driven in both directions by a crank and connecting rod, similar to the remains of a bellows system recorded at Cobscar Mill (3 kms to the south) in 1938.[10] It has been shown (above p.22) that there is no evidence for the London Lead Company's having pursued its interest in Grinton in 1733 and also that the mill was rebuilt in the early 19th century. Bellows, not blowing engines, are mentioned in sale documents in 1876 and 1888, although the term bellows might have been used for simplicity. Raistrick's suggested design for a blowing engine at Grinton should, therefore, be treated with caution.

No ore storage areas have been identified. It is possible that freestanding wooden storage bins existed in the furnace part of the mill building or that the building between this and the Peat House was for ore storage. The rubble spoil at the south of this structure contains small quantities of coal, but this may be later dumping.

Tyson and Spensley note that the present mill building appears to have been built prior to 1830, possibly in 1820-1822, and refurbished in c1890. A construction date of c1820 would not be architecturally out of place for the present building, but it is noticeable that its plan as shown by the OS in 1856 and 1893 was little, if any, changed from that of 1774. The main mill building was still T-shaped with a rectangular structure (the Peat House) to the east and suggestions of a flue, or group of flues, adjacent and parallel to the rectangular structure.

Plate 15. How smelt mill and peat house, looking south-west. (R.F. White, 1995).

The structural evidence of the mill does not obviously indicate rebuilding phases. The unconformity of the roofing courses might suggest that the two main parts of the mill building are of different date, but the joint details of the timber trusses are similar suggesting that any rebuild utilised trusses formed off-site. The joints of the principal walls also give a confusing picture, many faces being at best only partially tied into adjacent walls. A detailed analytical survey of the walls might enable construction and rebuilding phases to be worked out.

PEAT HOUSE

The Peat House is a near rectangular single storey building of mainly rubble limestone construction, with an arcade of four large, regularly spaced, arched openings on the north side. These are about 2.45 metres wide, but three have been partially blocked by drystone walling (plate 15). The internal area is around 21 metres by 4½ metres. Like the mill, the Peat House has a floor of rich organic earth, the top layer composed mainly of sheep droppings. Excavation during consolidation showed that this covers a layer of compressed peat which in turn overlies construction debris. There is a blocked arched opening on the gable nearest the mill and a small rectangular opening on the east gable. Two small rectangular openings on the west elevation are largely blocked by dry stone infill except for a narrow ventilation slit in each. Clough described them as chutes, but it is difficult to see how they could have been used for loading the peat house because of the flue.

The Peat House, also roofed with local stone slates in diminishing courses, had evidently been reslated prior to the consolidation programme. The apex of all nine principal sawn softwood trusses had moved some 0.45 metre to the west, but the purlins and the slating laths were still parallel with the main axis of the building, confirming that they had been replaced. The building had shifted to the south and west. That this movement was still occurring in 1990 could be seen by comparison of the freestanding blocking of the arcade and of the openings in the south wall with their surrounding walls and by cracks in the mortar of the 1977/8 repairs.

The site plan shows that the horizontal flue system of the mill passes immediately south of the Peat House building, an arrangement which has not been identified on any other Yorkshire lead smelting site. The lower part of the south wall of the Peat House was the north wall of the flue. The nature of this flue wall changed along the length of the peat house. The eastern five metre long section was arched, like the section which passes underneath the track east of the peat house, and continued to the chimney, but the western part of the flue had, it seemed, had a lintelled top. This wall had relatively shallow foundations – possibly partly the reason for the movement of the Peat House – but as no other foundations have been examined it is not known whether they differ from those of the rest of the building. On the basis of the structural detail of this wall, Francis and Cranstone suggest that the Peat House was part of the initial design of the flue (as built in its present form).[11] Prior to consolidation, the flue part of the wall had an almost dry stone appearance with some slight fume encrustation, contrasting with the almost flush white lime mortar with slag inclusions in the main part of the building.

The Peat House has obviously been considerably altered. The blockings of the arcade openings, of the western arch and of the rectangular openings above the flue are perhaps most likely to post date the abandonment of the building for peat storage and relate to its subsequent agricultural use. The alterations at the east gable, however, are likely to be earlier in date. As designed, this gable had been largely occupied by an opening extending to eaves height with access at internal ground level (now some 3.3 metres below eaves level). Externally, however, the ground level is only 1.4 to 1.8 metres below eaves level.

The large opening was presumably blocked to allow construction and use of the well graded track across the flue, immediately east of the peat house. This is the only crossing of the flue, other than a probable access beneath the flue immediately east of the mill, and is likely to have been an important route for bringing peat to the peat house from the moors to the south and east and for access to the Devis Hole lead mine, 400 metres to the south. However, the presence of a truss built into the east gable suggests that the alteration to the opening may have taken place during the construction phase. The opening in the blocking wall may be merely a window opening, but could also have functioned as a loading hole reached from the present track. The function of the block of coursed sandstone walling keyed into the eastern part of the north wall is unclear, but it could be the remains of an earlier buttress or an earlier structure on the site. The two buttresses on the south side of the Peat House clearly post date the abandonment of the flue.

THE FLUE

The flue extends east of the mill building, past the Peat House, under the track and rises 50 metres to the plateau on Sharrow Hill. It is 333 metres (1100 feet) long. It has partially collapsed, but surviving lengths are arched. For most of its length it is partly dug into the hillside and partly above ground. Internally it is approximately 1.8 metres high and 1.6 metres wide, but its height, width and section vary slightly, possibly a result of differential settling rather than as part of the design. When built, the flue would have been covered with soil, but today some of the stones forming the roof of the flue protrude, bristlelike, at the surface.

Eight openings (plate 16) are visible on the south side of the flue, irregularly spaced at intervals ranging from 14 metres to 42 metres. They vary in size, but range from 0.55 metre wide by 0.7 metre high to 0.65 metre square and are cut into the side of the flue at ground level. Vegetation changes and slight depressions suggest that there may have been another two openings. The present bottom of the flue is typically some 0.4 to 0.6 metre below the base of the openings. These have no obvious closing mechanisms, but temporary stone walling may have been used as required or metal plates or wooden boarding may have been used.

There are no such openings on the north side of the flue. It is likely, therefore, that the openings were for access and not as a means of controlling the draught. There are no surface leats providing a water supply for flushing nor any obvious settling ponds beside the flue. Francis's excavation of the flue beside the Peat House

Plate 16. How smelt mill: access hole in the flue. (R.F. White, 1995).

121

...vealed no evidence for a flagged floor. The traces of fume which were observed lay directly on a layer of clayey sand 0.25 metres below the present ground level.

The chimney is shown on the cover photograph, but only the footings and a low rubble spread survive. Clough says that it was nine feet square which is the external width (2.75 metres) of the eastern end as far as can be ascertained without excavation. There are no traces of any condenser buildings on the flue system.

The reference to the long length of new flue in 1892, noted by Tyson and Spensley, conflicts with the full length of the flue being shown in 1856, but may perhaps be evidence for repairs and a result of the later mill owners wishing to give a positive impression of their activities to potential investors.

THE WATER SUPPLY

The beck is dammed by a stone and earth bank, about one metre high above the present water level and 32 metres long. Two short lengths of vertical dressed sandstone rubble wall survive on either side of the beck, backed on the east by pitched sandstone blocks. The dam also seems to have been faced with pitched sandstone. Timbers in the beck immediately south of the dam may be the base of a sluice mechanism, or, more likely, the remains of an initial wooden dam.

The dammed area was relatively small. The 1891 map shows a triangular reservoir backing up for 35 metres but it incorporated, and was largely filled by, a strong spring, close to the bed of the beck. It was also fed by a similar sized reservoir, now silted up, 70 metres to the south west, as well as the headwaters of the beck.

The bed of the beck below the dam is formed of pitched sandstone blocks. Considerable areas of pitching still survive, but are obscured by later stream debris and, regrettably, by deliberate infilling by children and other visitors to the site.

OTHER EARTHWORKS

Most of the remains shown on the 1893 map can still be identified. The rectangular building south of the mill is marked as a smithy on the map. Surviving photographs of this building in the 1960s show a two-storey structure, but no obvious evidence for a blacksmith's hearth other than a chimney at the south end. The scale of the building suggests it may have also functioned as offices or, less likely in view of the proximity of Grinton village, as a lodging house. It now survives as a low pile of rubble with rear walls partly terraced into the hillside. The 1893 map shows what appears to be a wheel pit at the south end of the building, but no apparent head race. The pit still survives as a depression, some seven metres by 2½ metres, and the map shows two possible former exits for a tail race beside the beck, now visible as eroded hollows.

East of the 'smithy' and immediately north of the east end of the dam is another possible wheel pit, or more likely, a sluice channel, marked by a short length of dressed stone walling.

Unlike at many of the 19th century Yorkshire smelt mills, there are no extensive visible slag deposits, particularly of grey slag. A few fragments of black slag can be seen in the eroded sections west of the mill. Two vegetation-free areas north of the mill also contain fragments of grey slag. The apparent absence of slag could be due in part to its removal by school parties and other visitors to the site (much of the slag from Grinton smeltings has disappeared in this way over the last twenty years - Barker pers com), but the massive banks of black slag visible at e.g. Old Gang, The Octagon and CB New Mills are not particularly vulnerable to this process. Some slag may of course have been washed downstream.

THE LIME KILNS

The *'Old Limekiln'* on figures 12 & 13 to the north of the flue is now ruined, but two draw arches and a small, central arch survive. Lime was used in smelting and was also necessary for the construction of the mill buildings and flue, but the size of the kiln and quarry suggest that it was primarily a selling kiln. A mound 25 metres to the south of the main kiln is the remains of an another kiln marked by the 1st edition OS 6" map. McMahon (pers com) has identified the sites of at least three other kilns to the north. None are shown here on the 1774 map which only depicts one lime kiln elsewhere. A similar close relationship between lime kiln and smelt mill is found at Blakethwaite Mill in Gunnerside Gill, Swaledale.

LOGISTICAL PROBLEMS

The mill site was chosen and developed with some care, utilising its natural advantages, but in so doing the operators created problems for moving materials around the complex. Movement of men and materials would have been complicated by the presence of the flue and the water supply to the mill.

The principal access to the mill is via a graded track from the north. This opens out onto the mill terrace. If, as seems likely, and as shown by Clough, (cf Old Gang Upper or Old Mill in Swaledale and Providence Mill, Greenhow Hill), the flue was carried by an arch as it left the mill, this would give access all around the mill as there are doorways in all four sides of the building. This area is now a mound of rubble, but there are two lengths of short vertical walling, two metres apart, which may represent the sides of an arch. Such an arch would have assisted in the movement of peat from the Peat House on the upper terrace, possibly from the western (blocked) archway, under the flue and water supply, down to the hearths at the south end of the mill building. There is, however, no clearly defined path down from the north side of the Peat House to the Mill. A peat chute may have been used, but there is no documentary or field evidence for one. The lines on the 1893 map (fig.12) crossing (under?) the leat suggest two possible short lengths of tramway, but these lead towards the track to the north.

It is also unclear how the water supply to the waterwheel negotiated the flue. Much of the headrace still survives as a shallow depression, but immediately south west of the Peat House this is at approximately the same level as the base of the flue. It is possible that the race was carried through the flue in a sealed wooden or metal pipe, but more likely that the leat ran underneath the flue. Excavation ld be necessary to confirm this. The 1893 map shows the leat leading west of the smithy building. North of the Peat House, a shallow depression marks the overflow course of the leat for when the wheel was taken out of use.

THE CONSOLIDATION PROGRAMME

EMERGENCY WORKS

The scheduling of the complex in 1975 gave an impetus for consolidation of the mill building. Largely at the instigation of the Swaledale National Park Warden, Lawrence Barker, the Yorkshire Dales National Park Authority instigated further discussions with the landowner and tenant and with the then Department of the Environment (DoE) and began a consolidation programme (plate 17).

The DoE offered a 50 per cent grant towards the costs of essential repairs to the flue egress from the mill, the western furnace arch and the corner of the Peat House, estimated to cost £1850 in December 1976. It also offered the services of its in-house skilled staff to do the work and estimated that a full preservation scheme *"to ancient monuments standards would cost £37,000-43,000."*

The work was done by DoE field staff in April - July 1977, with extra work to the south east and south west corners of the Peat House, again 50 per cent grant aided by the Authority, at a total cost of £2650. More repairs, to the roof above the flue egress from the mill building, were done by DoE staff at the Authority's expense in early 1978 (£517.45; wrongly dated as 1980 in White 1989). As part of this work the eastern lintel between the furnace backs and the cross-wall was replaced and the corework between and above the hearths consolidated.

THE MILL

In 1981 further discussion about consolidation took place between the DoE and the National Park. Roger Wools, then of NYCC Planning Department, prepared detailed specifications for the complete reroofing of the mill building; relaying the existing, diminishing coursed, stone flag roof on new laths and including a reconstruction of the previously repaired section of roof at the flue egress; comprehensive timber treatment; selective repointing and the replacement of limited small areas of missing or defective stonework; repairs to damaged stone cills; rebuilding of the doorway arch at the south west corner; partial rebuilding of the wall immediately south of the flue egress to receive the new roof timbers proposed here; and insertion of guard rails to prevent visitors from accidentally falling from the flue to the floor of the mill. The specifications also proposed the selective clearing of grassed over mounds of rubble below the line of the flue on the east side of the mill and at the north east corner.

Scheduled Monument Consent was received for these works in June 1982. In order to safeguard its proposed investment in the mill complex, the Authority sought to enter into a management agreement with the owner and tenant, under Section 17 of the 1979 Ancient Monuments and Archaeological Areas Act. A detailed agreement was finally concluded in January 1987. Attached to this was

Plate 17. How smelt mill: emergency consolidation work, 1977. (YDNP, 1977).

a brief management plan, the aim being *"the continued survival, as buildings and structures of the complex known as Grinton Smelt Mill, relic of the lead mining and smelting industry"*.

The schedule of proposed conservation works to the mill had been agreed with the owner and quotations were subsequently sought from eight local building contractors. Four contractors submitted quotations, ranging from £9806 to £18,395. R & DS Parker were awarded the contract for the works which were carried out in May 1987. The consolidation specifications had been drawn up in 1982. Deterioration had continued in the intervening period and more extensive exterior pointing was carried out, together with the provision of black painted mild steel straps to support the remains of the leat feeding the overshot waterwheel, and support to the furnace wall below the new guard rails. A 40 per cent grant towards the costs of the work was given by English Heritage. The *'selective clearance'* was considered to be unnecessary for the protection of the structure and was not carried out. Subsequent investigation here suggests that the mound is bounded by curved in-situ walling.

THE BECK
At the same time, the contractor cleared a 15 metre length of the beck south of the mill of boulder infill, revealing the side walls of the collapsed culvert and a pitched stone bed. The existing, southern end of the culvert was consolidated by being backed with reinforced concrete and covered with turves, and a partially

125

apsed section north of the mill was also consolidated by reinforced concrete. ...e then north end of the culvert was later consolidated by National Park field staff owing to collapses caused by petty vandalism.

THE PEAT HOUSE

While Messrs Parker were on site, a more detailed inspection of the Peat House revealed that the central buttress was in imminent danger of collapse and consequently stabilisation works were carried out here. This included the rebuilding of two buttresses and the installation of temporary raking trusses to help support the existing, failed, roof trusses. This was in advance of the preparation of comprehensive proposals for the consolidation of the Peat House.

This temporary measure lessened the likelihood of imminent collapse, but the building was still visibly deteriorating. The preparation of consolidation proposals was less straightforward than for the mill.

It was decided, following the principle of *'consolidate as found'*, to attempt to retain the existing leaning character and, where possible, the original timberwork of the building. The eventual solution, arrived at after much discussion between YDNP staff and English Heritage engineers, notably Ian Hume, was to insert four reinforced concrete buttresses, hidden inside the rubble core of the south wall of the building and linked to a reinforced concrete ring beam, again set into the rubble core, at the top of the walls. These buttresses had base pads set outside the south wall to counteract the lean of the building, the reinforcement being passed underneath the outer face of the wall. The buttresses were inserted by removing a narrow section of the face of the wall inside the building to remove the rubble core and rebuilding the face of the wall. They were then cast, in situ, in stages. The existing failed roof trusses were then supplemented by the insertion of nine new oak raking trusses, or braces, at each original truss to create axio-eccentric pyramid trusses bearing on the new ring beam. The new trusses were bolted onto the existing purlins, thus making a very rigid structure. The major part of the building was also repointed and the roof relaid.

As part of the implementation of these works, the Cranstone Consultancy was commissioned to prepare a detailed record of the building, utilising rectified photography, and to excavate the base pads for the concrete buttresses. This work was supervised by Antony Francis and much of the above description of the building is based on the archive report prepared by him and David Cranstone.[10] Four small trenches were excavated across the flue in advance of the installation of the reinforced buttresses. These were each two metres by one metre in area and 0.8 metre deep and cut through the line of the flue, exposing its southern wall built of sandstone rubble. The shallow, slightly concave, pre-excavation ground profile and the limited amount of rubble found in the trenches suggests that this length of flue had been intentionally demolished or robbed. No evidence for a flagged floor was found and the fume deposits observed lay directly on a clayey sand floor.

126

Francis and Cranstone suggest that the fume encrustment on some of the blocks of the secondary buttresses, which now partly support the south wall of the Peat House, may indicate that part of the flue was re-used for these buttresses.

As yet no work has been done on the flue system. There is now very little soil or vegetation cover on top of the flue and it is collapsing, particularly at the exposed ends and around some of the eight access hatches on the south side of the flue. It is suffering from a combination of natural decay and from being used as a walkway both by sheep and visitors. The latter now play as important a part in the economy of the Yorkshire Dales as the lead industry once did. It is, however, hoped to devise an acceptable means of protecting the flue and to carry out further work on the culvert and smithy building, as well as to provide some on-site interpretation to aid public understanding and protection of the Grinton complex – the most-visited lead smelting mill in the Yorkshire Dales.

ACKNOWLEDGEMENTS
Much of the above note is based on the work of Francis, Cranstone and Turnbull for the Yorkshire Dales National Park. I am grateful to them, to Richard Lamb for making his drawings of the mill available and bringing the 1774 map and the similarities of the Percy slag hearth to my attention, and in particular to Lawrence Barker for initiating the consolidation work at Grinton, introducing me to the lead industry and freely sharing his knowledge. My understanding of the mill has benefited greatly from discussions with them all; any misinterpretations and errors in this note are my own.

REFERENCES

1. NYCRO. ZRT 2/3. MIC 2120. PRO. MPE 390.

2. Clough, R.T. "The Lead Smelting Mills of Yorkshire, Part III, Swaledale and Arkengarth-dale" *Cave Science*, Vol.2 No.9 (1949), pp.31-42.

3. Clough, R.T. *The Lead Smelting Mills of the Yorkshire Dales* (Keighley: R.T. Clough, 1962).

4. Clough, R.T. *The Lead Smelting Mills of the Yorkshire Dales and Northern Pennines* (Keighley: R.T. Clough, 1980).

5. White, R.F. "Conservation of the Remains of the Lead Industry in the Yorkshire Dales" *Industrial Archaeology Review*, Vol.xii, Part i (1989), pp.94-104.

6. Turnbull, P. "Grinton Smelt Mill, Swaledale", (Unpublished report for the Yorkshire Dales National Park, 1994).

7. Percy, J. *Metallurgy: Vol.3 Pt 2 Lead* (Eindhoven: Der Archaeologische Pers, 1986. Reprint of 1870 Edition).

8. Raistrick, A. *The Lead Industry of Wensleydale and Swaledale Volume 2, The Smelting Mills* (Hartington: Moorland, 1975). Fig.12.

9. Lamb, R. "A Smelting Miscellany" pp.35-36, in Willies, L. and Cranstone, D. (Eds) *Boles and Smeltmills* (Matlock Bath: Historical Metallurgy Society, 1992).

10. Woodall, F. "Early Smelt Mill Bellows" *Industrial Archaeology*, Vol.15 No.4 (1980), pp.291-294.

11. Francis, A. & Cranstone, D. *Grinton Peat Store. The 1992 Season: Archive Report.* (Typescript report for Yorkshire Dales National Park, 1992).

PRODUCTION FIGURES FOR THE GRINTON MINES

OUTPUT OF LEAD FROM GRINTON, WHITASIDE & HARKERSIDE

	Pieces	Tons
1775	1651	108.97
1776	1562	103.42
1777	2517	168.86
1778	1500	99.30
1779	1600	107.04
1780	1954	129.34
1781	1325	87.81
1782	1576	104.79
1783	1215	81.46
1784	600	40.06
1785	518	35.42
1786	662	44.45
1787	528	35.75
1788	239	15.96
1789	595	40.14
1790	1110	78.27
1791/2	500	35.44
1793	1000	70.42
1794	569	40.40
1795/6	625	44.24
1796	500	34.88
1797	1000	70.78
1798	1000	70.73
1798/9	2000	142.01
1799	2000	142.21
1800	4500	316.48
1801	770	54.61

Public Records Office Ref. No's Cres 2/1390 & LR5/9 XC 0629.

Whitaside			Pieces	Tons
1801 23rd Feby	-	23rd July 1804	3582	253.98
1804 23rd July	-	23rd July 1805	143	10.14
1805 23rd July	-	23rd July 1806	702	49.13
1806 23rd July	-	23rd July 1807	1292	91.01
1810 23rd July	-	23rd July 1812	952	67.11

Summer Lodge			Pieces	Tons
1810 23rd July	-	23rd July 1811	1616	114.43
1811 23rd July	-	23rd July 1812	4796	343.23
1812 23rd July	-	23rd July 1813	9406	675.01

Public Records Office Ref. No. LR 5/9. XC 0629.

LEAD RAISED AND SMELTED FROM SUMMER LODGE LEAD MINE
(under a lease for 12 years from 1/1/1808, from Mrs Mary Knighton
and Josias Readshaw Morley Esq. to June 28th 1817)

Year	Pieces	Tons
1809	18	1.23
1810	1653	117.07
1811	4921	351.78
1812	8880	638.82
1813	8258	594.15
1814	3432	249.92
1815	6193	453.53
1816	7837	577.06
1817	1596	118.75

Lead raised and smelted from the sundry old wastes and mines in the Manor of Grinton to June 28th 1817.

Year	Pieces	Tons
1810	368	26.04
1811	252	17.56
1812	49	3.47
1814		18.51
1815		6.65
1816		15.30
1817		5.38
	Total produced	92.90 tons.

Public Records Office Ref. No. LR 5/9. XC 0629.

ORE FROM GRINTON MINES SMELTED AT:

	Smelt Mill	Pieces	Tons
1820	Apedale	40	2.86
	Grove Beck	18	1.38
	Summer Lodge	80	5.95
	Surrender	47	3.60
		185	13.79
1821	Apedale	82	5.78
	Cobscar	6	0.43
	Grove Beck	90	6.86
	Summer Lodge	250	18.57
	Surrender	133	10.36
		561	42.00
1822	Apedale	33	2.33
	Cobscar	2	0.14
	Grove Beck	106	8.09
	Summer Lodge	243	18.10
	Surrender	16	1.20
		400	29.86

Public Records Office Ref. No. Cres 34/214. File 1881/3.

LEAD PRODUCED AT GRINTON MINES 1820-1875

Year	Start		End	Pieces	Tons	Value (£)
1820				185	13.79	
1821				561	42.00	
1822				400	29.86	
1833	3rd Dec	-	10th Oct 1835	-	-	1672.04
1835	10th Oct	-	10th Oct 1836	-	-	817.54
1836	10th Oct	-	5th Jan 1839	-	-	1883.50
1839	5th Jan	-	5th Jan 1840	-	-	7534.30
1840	5th Jan	-	5th Jan 1841	-	-	3025.72
1841	5th Jan	-	10th Oct 1841	765	58.29	990.38
1841	10th Oct	-	10th Oct 1842	1322	101.74	1600.75
1843	10th Oct	-	10th Oct 1844	3721	282.62	4171.59
1844	10th Oct	-	10th Oct 1845	2702	205.24	3268.74
1845	10th Oct	-	10th Oct 1846	-	-	1727.72
1846	10th Oct	-	10th Oct 1847	2006	151.04	2225.04
1847	10th Oct	-	10th Oct 1848	-	-	2937.73
1848	10th Oct	-	10th Oct 1849	2969	227.51	3154.11
1849	28th Mar	-	30th Jun 1850	1647	125.22	
1849	10th Oct	-	10th Oct 1850	-	-	5040.99
1850	10th Oct	-	10th Oct 1851	3199	248.65	3481.07
1851	10th Oct	-	10th Oct 1852	2100	162.00	2872.48
1852	10th Jan	-	10th Oct 1853	-	-	4983.71
1853	10th Jan	-	10th Oct 1854	4900	374.69	1723.23
1855	5th Jan	-	5th Jan 1856	-	-	4215.20
1856	5th Jan	-	5th Jan 1857	-	-	3602.58
1857	5th Jan	-	5th Jan 1858	-	-	5799.85
1858	5th Jan	-	5th Jan 1859	-	-	5401.38
1859	5th Jan	-	5th Jan 1860	-	-	2239.18
1860	5th Jan	-	26th Aug 1861	-	-	-
1861	26th Aug	-	5th Jan 1862	-	-	2650.10
1862	5th Jan	-	5th Jan 1863	-	-	2060.55
1863	5th Jan	-	5th Jan 1864	-	-	1708.68
1864	5th Jan	-	5th Jan 1865	-	-	1417.20
1865	5th Jan	-	5th Jan 1866	-	-	2800.44
1866	5th Jan	-	5th Jan 1867	-	-	2868.72
1867	5th Jan	-	5th Jan 1868	-	-	3258.84
1868	5th Jan	-	5th Jan 1869	-	-	2160.48
1869	5th Jan	-	5th Jan 1870	-	-	2849.40
1870	5th Jan	-	5th Jan 1871	-	-	2339.52
1871	5th Jan	-	5th Jan 1872	-	-	1342.56
1872	5th Jan	-	5th Jan 1873	-	-	535.20
1873	5th Jan	-	5th Jan 1874	-	-	497.76
1874	5th Jan	-	5th Jan 1875	-	-	175.20
1875	5th Jan	-	5th Jan 1876	-	-	196.68

Public Records Office Ref. Nos: Cres 34/214 (File 1881/3); Cres 2/1390; Cres 2/1391; Durham Records Office Ref. No. D/HH/6/4/32.

COPY OF SEVERAL ACCOUNTS
IN THE POSSESSION OF WILLIAM CHAYTOR Esq.,
(and paid by him for and on account of the Crown Duty Lead).

No 13.   Account sales of three hundred & eighty four pieces of lead
received from William Chaytor, Esq., Spennithorn.

Stamped	Letters	Pieces	Tons	Cwt	qtr	lbs			
SLCo & GR.	E-Q	384	28	04	00	08			
							£	s	d
at £27 for 2464 lbs (22 cwt)							692	05	04

Charges.	£	s	d			
Paid George Harker for weighing		17	01			
Paid Geo Harker for Piling		04	09			
Paid Geo Harker for setting up						
Skales, Postage etc.		06	04			
Commission.	6	18	04	8	06	06
Paid J. Place & John Hird for carriage						
of the above from Summer Lodge Mill						
to Borobridge at 46 shillings per score				44	02	06
				639	16	04

The above Lead sold at Borobridge.
Leyburn May 28th 1813. John Renney.

Public Records Office Ref. No. LR5/9. XC 0629.